CLIMATE

CO$_2$

NATURE'S GIFT

JEREMY NIEBOER

www.brugesgroup.com

Published in 2022 by The Bruges Group, 246 Linen Hall, 162-168 Regent Street, London W1B 5TB

Follow us on Twitter @brugesgroup, LinkedIn @brugesgroup, GETTR @brugesgroup

Facebook The Bruges Group, Instagram brugesgroup, YouTube brugesgroup

ABOUT THE AUTHOR

JEREMY NIEBOER was educated at Harrow School and Oriel College Oxford. After a period practising as a member of the Bar in Kings Bench Walk he was then admitted as a solicitor becoming a partner in two City law firms. He specialised in corporate work including mergers and acquisitions, capital market public offerings, private equity transactions and commercial law. He still acts for a few long-standing clients. His first encounter with any challenge to the accepted doctrine of 'global warming' came through his contact with Christopher Booker whom Jeremy first met when acting as lead solicitor on the application to the High Court by Lord Rees-Mogg to restrain ratification of the Maastricht Treaty. Christopher himself published his essential work "The Real Global Warming Disaster" in 2009. Just at the time of its publication there was public meeting in Church House addressed by Professor Plimer in which he succinctly set out the fundamental scientific flaws of alleged CO_2 driven global warming. It was this that set Jeremy on a path of enquiry and research. He has been a lead speaker at public meetings and debates on the want of any tenable scientific basis for the demonisation of CO_2 and the falsehood of global warming theory.

He published his first booklet on climate alarmism in 2010 "A Lesson in Democracy". His book "CLIMATE All is Well All will be Well" was published in October 2021 and became the Number One Best Seller in Amazon's Climate Change and Ecology category. It was described by William Happer Professor Emeritus of Physics Princeton University USA as *"excellent"* and by Michel Van Biezen Professor of Physics at Loyola Mount University USA as *"impressive"*.

FOREWORD

The dogma of 'global warming' was conceived as a means of socialist reversal of the global economic order. It was adopted 45 years ago by a group at Stanford University USA led by Stephen Schneider Professor of Environmental Biology and Global Change. He declared that

"In searching for a new enemy to unite us, we came up with the idea that pollution, the threat of global warming, water shortages, famine and the like would fit the bill.

He himself well knew that CO_2 could not cause this[1]. Yet he cynically demonised it recognizing that fossil fuels were the foundation of the growth and prosperity of capitalist economies. By demonising the CO_2 that combustion emitted the economic sub structure of the west could be dismantled.

"To capture the public imagination we have to offer up some scary scenarios, make simple dramatic statements and little mention of any doubts one might have. Each of us has to strike the right balance between being effective and being honest[2]"

'Climate Change' dogma took hold through gross distortions of science for political ends. It was largely the work of one Maurice Strong[3] an extreme socialist who owed his great wealth to the oil industry. He had close life long business and financial links with China where he lived for years and which he regarded as an ideal society. He held senior posts in the United Nations. He founded the UN Environment Programme and initiated the UN Intergovernmental Panel on Climate Change' (IPCC) to promote the dogma of man made dangerous global warming due to CO_2 emissions.

The entire base and fabric of the IPCC dangerous warming dogma rests upon the colossal falsehood that rising atmospheric CO_2 since 1890 has created a trap for heat from the Earth's surface which is accumulating to such an extent as to threaten humanity's very existence.

This book demonstrates that such claim is without any foundation in physics and chemistry. It describes how doubling CO_2 will have no noticeable effect on the temperature of the Earth. It explains how CO_2 is the key to mankind's very existence, welfare and prosperity.

CO_2 with H_2O keeps Earth's average temperature of 15^0C with no 'trap' or 'blanket'.

CO_2 at 50% of today's level is saturated with Earth's radiation and cannot absorb more heat from it.

CO_2 and H_2O absorbed solar energy radiates to space cooling the atmosphere by convection.

CO_2 with H_2O and sunlight provides the store of energy for all plants and trees.

CO_2 synthesis with light and H_2O provides all of the oxygen that we breathe.

CO_2 atmospheric increases are extending vast regions of grass and crops in drought drylands.

CO_2 has optimum levels of up to 3 times those of today. These double crop yields.

CO_2 does not pollute. Each of us breathes out over I kg of CO_2 every day.

CO2 is the very breath of plants that feed animals and all mankind.

Can it be doubted that CO_2 is the generous gift of providence and a blessing for all humanity.

---

[1] The *"greenhouse effect will not occur because the 15 micron CO_2 band, which is the main source of absorption is saturated,* 'Rasool, S.I., and. Schneider S.H 1971: Atmospheric carbon dioxide and aerosols: Effects of large increases on global climate. *Science*, 173, 138-141.
[2] Dr Stephen Schneider "Discover" October 1989.
[3] 1929 – 2015. President Power Corpn of Canada 1966. :Secretary General of the UN Conference on the Human Environment : first executive director of the UN Environment Programme. CEO Petro-Canada and chairman Ontario Hydro.

CONTENTS

FIGURES

ABSTRACT

Carbon provides the structure and the means of nutrition for all humanity, animals and plants. It forms 45% of Earth's dry biomass and 67% of dry weight of our bodies.

CO_2, with light and water, creates the food of trees and plants and so of all humanity. It produces the oxygen we breathe. All living creatures depend on CO_2 for life. It keeps the Earth at an average 15^{0}C. It forms 417 parts per million (ppm) of the air – just 0.0417%.

It is not a pollutant.

6% of solar energy radiates back from the Earth to warm molecules of H_2O and CO_2. H_2O accounts for 75% of the greenhouse effect – CO_2 for 20%. CO_2 absorbs this energy only in quanta and only in restricted wavelengths of 14 – 16 microns.

Surface energy absorbed by CO_2 rises up 15km - 20km by convection where it radiates to space causing down convection of cold air to cool the lower atmosphere. CO_2 has consistent density throughout the atmosphere. It does not form a 'trap' or a blanket.

Saturation of CO_2 with surface radiation means that once over 250 ppm it has only been able to absorb negligible surface energy. Doubling CO_2 from today's level of 417ppm will raise global temperature by less than 1^{0}C and is of no consequence.

There has been no causal link of temperature and CO_2 density over 600m years or in any recent time. There is a close link of temperature with solar activity. Warming since 1800 is due to solar activity. There has been a fall in temperature of 0.22^{o}C since 1998. Over the 42 years since 1980 temperature has risen by just 0.27^{0}C.

For 395m of 400m years since plants appeared CO_2 density has been up to 8 times higher than now. If CO_2 levels decline to 200ppm - just 80ppm lower than its pre- industrial level – crop growth and yields will fall by 40% - 70% in one generation.

Increased atmospheric CO_2 has accounted for at least 70% of satellite recorded global increased greening. Rise of CO_2 density to 1000-1200 ppm increases crop yields by up to 100 percent and raises the ideal temperature for photosynthesis.

UN data on crop production for 1961 – 2011 show a calculated value of higher crop yields of $3.2 trillion due to rising CO_2. Estimates to 2050 are more than double that value.

Carbon dioxide is the most potent natural force for the relief of world hunger and poverty.

It is indispensable to our existence.

SUMMARY OF CONTENTS

The abandonment since 2013 of our reserves of coal, oil and gas as the basis of generation of electricity has deprived the UK of energy self sufficiency. It has exposed us to rocketing prices for gas on global markets. No adequate, secure and reliable energy source is available at economic cost. Vast subsidies alone sustain wind and sun power imposing heavy levies on consumers.

Electricity generation that depends on atmospheric pressure is inadequate both in reliability, efficiency and cost. It cannot be stored. Sun panels depend on the extent of cloud cover. They are diurnal – there is no power for half the year. Wind turbines depend on correct wind velocity. In storms and on days of high pressure they are of no use. We depend on gas to maintain supply.

In 2020 just 13.7% of UK primary energy[5] was from low carbon sources[6]. Only 4% of power generation was provided by wind. Sun power was a mere 0.7%. 6.6% was from nuclear.

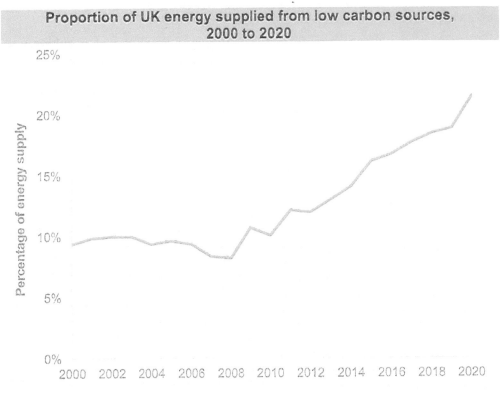

	2000	2005	2010	2018	2019	Percentage 2020
Nuclear	8.4%	7.8%	6.3%	7.4%	6.5%	6.6%
Wind	0.0%	0.1%	0.4%	2.6%	3.0%	4.0%
Solar	0.0%	0.0%	0.0%	0.6%	0.6%	0.7%
Hydro	0.2%	0.2%	0.1%	0.2%	0.3%	0.4%
Bioenergy	0.9%	1.6%	2.3%	6.1%	6.7%	7.8%
Transport fuels	0.0%	0.0%	0.6%	0.7%	0.9%	1.0%
Other	0.0%	0.0%	0.4%	0.8%	0.9%	1.0%
Total	**9.4%**	**9.7%**	**10.1%**	**18.5%**	**18.9%**	**21.5%**

[5] An energy form found in nature that has not been subjected to any human engineered conversion process.
[6] UK Energy in Brief 2021.BEIS latest national statistics www.gov.uk/government/statistics/uk-energy-in-brief-2021

Yet since 2000 UK oil production has fallen by 62% with our gas down by 65% and coal by 94%.[1]

No material increase in power generation by sun panels and wind turbines will be possible without massive capital initial expenditure. Subsidies already are now so high as to inflict on domestic electricity users a levy of at least 25% in addition to the VAT charge. We cannot afford the shocking cost for such little benefit.

The UK is now a net importer of all main fuel types comprising 35% of pre-Covid levels of demand. That percentage has increased significantly since the end of the Covid contraction.

This grave and harmful predicament has not been inflicted by war. It has not been dictated by exhaustion of resources.

It has been imposed without national debate.

Its consequence is the most steep and sudden increase in the costs of normal life and decline in standards of living since the Second World War.

This disaster – for such it is – has been brought down upon us solely by blind obeisance to the dogma of global warming. It has eliminated scientific enquiry and tolerates no dissent.

That dogma depends on a single paramount falsehood. It is that carbon dioxide is a pollutant that acts as a 'blanket' to 'trap' heat radiated by Earth's surface so causing warming of the planet to an extent that imperils the very existence of humanity.

It is that colossal falsehood that this book seeks to expose.

Part 1   Describes the nature, properties and innumerable uses of the element Carbon and its astonishing compound carbon dioxide (CO_2). Included are explanations of how carbon provides the structure and the means of nutrition for all humanity, animals and plants. The oxygen we breathe we owe to photosynthesis of CO_2, sugar and H_2O. **To remove carbon is to eliminate life.**

Part 2   Explains how CO_2 and H_2O keep Earth's temperature at 15^0C. Shows how greenhouse gasses absorb just 6% of solar energy from which CO_2 creates 20% of the greenhouse effect. Explains how absorbed solar energy rising by convection allows radiation to space at higher altitudes and cooling by descending cold air. **Describes how saturation of the absorption wavelength bands with radiation means that doubling CO_2 only causes a 1% rise in temperature ($3Wm^2$) or no more than 1^0C.**

Part 3   Shows that there is no causal correlation between increases in CO_2 and temperature. It defines the close correlation of temperature with solar activity. It demonstrates the invalidity of climate models of past temperature and the distortions of predicted temperature. It explains how satellite data show that temperature has risen by just 0.27% since 1980 and that there has been no warming trend since 1998.

Part 4   Describes the miracle of photosynthesis of Nature using CO_2 sunlight and water to form sugar and starch in plants as energy stores. Transpiration, respiration and photorespiration are explained and how present CO_2 levels are 3 times lower than optimum. It explains the devastating effects on growth and survival of plants of falling levels of CO_2 and shows how rises in CO_2 result in abundant crop yields and values.

The appalling events in the Ukraine have shocked Western democracies. Yet they have allowed reality to assume dominion over wishful thought. It is clear to all but the most obsessed that we must regain self sufficiency in energy – energy that is abundant and affordable.

This can only be guaranteed by exploiting the fossil fuels that lie under the surface of our land and seas in the knowledge that emissions of CO_2 can only be of benefit to all humanity.

---

[1] UK Energy in Brief 2021.

PART 1

If you control Carbon you control Life
Richard Lindzen[8]

I.   CARBON

Carbon is a chemical element having the symbol C. It owes its name to the Latin for coal *'carbo'*. It is non metallic. It is quadrivalent so that it makes four electrons available to form chemical bonds.

Carbon is the fourth most abundant element in the universe by mass after hydrogen, helium, and oxygen. Carbon's abundance, its diversity of organic compounds[9], and its capacity to form polymers[10] ensure that it is a common element of all known life. It represents approximately 45%– 50% of all dry biomass of the Earth.

Carbon forms approximately 550 billion tons of the forms of life on the planet[11]. Carbon in the human body includes carbon dioxide, proteins, carbohydrates, lipids[12], and nucleic acids. It is the second most abundant element in the body by mass at about 18.5% after oxygen. It forms 67% dry weight of our bodies since it is water that accounts for the predominance of oxygen.

The physical properties of carbon are capable of extreme variation. Graphite is opaque and black while diamond is highly transparent and brilliant. Graphite is so soft that is smears paper. Diamond is the hardest naturally occurring material. Graphite is a good electrical conductor while diamond has a low electrical conductivity.

Carbon constitutes about 12% by mass of the Earth's masses of carbonate rock particularly chalk, limestone, dolomite and marble. Coal is rich in carbon with anthracite containing 92%–98%. It is the largest commercial source of mineral carbon, accounting for 4,000 gigatonnes or 80% of fossil fuel.

It has been estimated that the terrestrial Earth contains 730 parts per million of carbon, with 2000 ppm in the core and 120 ppm in the combined mantle and crust. This suggests an amount of 4360 million gigatonnes[13] of carbon. Soils – particularly arctic soils – vegetation and humus contain far more carbon pat 2000 bn tons than all carbon in living matter and the atmosphere[14].

The oceans of the planet contain approximately 40,000 bn tonnes of carbon.

Whilst the atmosphere contains the equivalent of 800bn tons of carbon this is just 0.001% of total carbon in the whole biospheric system of upper crust, oceans and the air[15].

---

8 Alfred P Sloan Professor in Atmospheric Physics at the Massachusetts Institute of Technology and previous professorships at Harvard University and the University of Chicago. Gave evidence to House of Lords Select Committee on Economic Affairs 25 October 2005.
9 Chemical compounds that contain carbon-hydrogen bonds. Living things incorporate inorganic carbon compounds into organic compounds through photosynthesis.
10 A substance with very large molecules of many repeating subunits.[6] Polymers are essential for daily life and range from familiar synthetic plastics such as polystyrene to natural fundamental biological biopolymers including DNA and proteins.
11 Reece, Jane B. (31 October 2013). *Campbell Biology* (10 ed.). Pearson. ISBN 9780321775658.
12 Organic compounds for storing energy, signalling, and acting as structural components of cell membranes.
13 Gigaton = one billion tons.
14 Batjes NH *Total carbon and nitrogen in the soils of the world,* European Journal of Soil Sciences 47, pp305 – 310 cited in *Heaven and Earth Global Warming the Missing Science*. Professor Ian Plimer 2009 Connor Court Publishing at p415
15 Professor Plimer *Heaven and Earth* 2009 Connor Court Publishing Pty p412.

The Slow Geological Carbon Cycle

There is vast and constant movement of carbon between the lithosphere[16], hydrosphere, biosphere and the atmosphere. The slow carbon cycle is the outcome of solar energy and the water cycle.

Carbon from the atmosphere moves to the hydrosphere through the combining of carbon and water from the atmosphere to form weak carbonic acid which over large time scales dissolves rocks in the lithosphere into soil by chemical weathering. Carbon so released into the oceans to the extent not taken up by the atmosphere is ultimately stored in limestone calcium carbonate. There is a balance between the process of sedimentation in the form of carbon export to the ocean floor and remineralization in the form of the release of carbon to the atmosphere.

The lithosphere holds most of the store of carbon of the planet. Volcanic eruptions, vast tectonic shifts and subduction by collision of plates all result in emission of CO_2 into the atmosphere. Visible volcanoes represent only 15% of the Earth's total with 85% being submarine.

The formation of the Himalayas by collision of the Indian and Eurasian tectonic plates resulted in the exposure of vast amounts of sedimentary rock layers including limestone, marble and shale. Chemical weathering of such rocks has contributed considerably to the geological carbon cycle.

The hydrosphere participates extensively in the slow geological carbon cycle. It does so by the absorption characteristics of the oceans. Cold water at the poles absorbs CO_2 but with increase in surface temperature the ocean becomes saturated and releases dissolved CO_2. The ocean absorbs atmospheric carbon dioxide into what is known as the mixed layer being a thin layer of water with nearly uniform temperature, salinity, and dissolved gases. Wind-driven turbulence maintains the mixed layer in this composition by stirring for the water near the ocean's surface.

Over a much longer term, carbon dioxide slowly enters the deep ocean at the bottom of the mixed layer. It also sinks in regions near the poles as cold, salty water descends to the depths. It is very slowly conveyed to the tropics for up to 1000 years or more when it gradually upwells.

The oceans take up carbon dioxide through photosynthesis by phytoplankton – small plant-like organisms – and also be by simple chemistry. Carbon dioxide dissolves in water. It reacts with seawater, creating carbonic acid. Carbonic acid releases hydrogen ions, which combine with carbonate in seawater to form bicarbonate.

However, the warmer the surface water becomes, the process of mixing of the surface layers with the deeper layers diminishes. The ocean settles into layers or 'stratifies'. Without an infusion of fresh carbonate-rich water from below, the surface water saturates with carbon dioxide. The stagnant water also supports fewer phytoplankton and carbon dioxide uptake from photosynthesis slows. Stratification results in a steady leaking out of CO_2 into the atmosphere.

Uses and applications of Carbon

Carbon provides the structure and the means of nutrition for all humanity, animals and plants.

It has innumerable uses for mankind. It is revealing how many applications and processes of our modern existence depend on this priceless element.

---

[16] Earth's rigid crust and the top part of the upper mantle.

These include motive and thermal power as coal, oil, natural gas, petrochemicals including polymers, fibres, paints, solvents and plastics, smelting coke, furnace linings, beverages, electric motor brushes, sugars, lignans[17], chitins[18], alcohols, fats, refrigerants, filters of all kinds, tennis rackets, fishing rods, rockets, insulation, abrasives, superlubricitous lubricants, conductors, aircraft, bearings, steel, industrial saws, polishers and drills, wine, pneumatic systems, fire extinguishers, battery electrolytes, solvents, printing inks, coolants, textiles and leather, cleaning and surface preparation, life rafts and life jackets, pulp and paper, enhanced oil recovery, water treatment, baking soda, electronic components, Alka Seltzer, purification and nanotechhology applications including carbon nanotubes, other fullerenes and atom-thin sheets of graphene.

Carbon compounds

Carbon is unique in the variety of ways that it can combine with other elements. The majority of all known compounds contain carbon. Its key to the chemistry of life is the facility of each carbon atom simultaneously to form up to four valence bonds[19] with other atoms.

Furthermore the energy required to make or break a bond with a carbon atom is such as enables the building of large complex molecules. The ease with which carbon atoms bond to other carbon atoms results in the building of long macromolecules and polymers.

The adult human body averages 53% water (H_2O) and for this reason it contains more oxygen by mass than any element. However 67% of the body consists of carbon dry weight.

Carbon compound biological macromolecules are vital to living organisms. They include:-

- Carbohydrates: stores of energy available to living cells.
- Lipids: dense stores of energy available for long periods in the bodies of animals.
- Proteins: building blocks of living organisms including most enzymes which catalyse organic chemical reactions the most common being RuBisCO.
- Nucleic acids: the conveyors of genetic information.

10,000,000 compounds have been so far identified. One of the simplest class of carbon compounds is the hydrocarbons. These consist of the element carbon in combination with the element hydrogen. Yet hydrocarbon compounds extend to $C_{30}H_{62}$. There is a scarcely credible number of possible molecules made from carbon and hydrogen combinations. The C_{30} hydrocarbons alone (diesel fuels/lubricating oils) with the maximum number of hydrogens – 62 in all which all have the formula $C_{30}H_{62}$ – comprise over 4bn possibilities.

SUMMARY

Carbon provides the structure and the means of nutrition for all humanity, animals and plants. Due to carbon's abundance, organic compounds[20], and capacity to create polymers it forms 45%– 50% of all dry biomass of the Earth. It has innumerable uses. Its compounds are vital to life. It is the second most abundant element in the human body by mass after oxygen and 67% of its dry weight.

---

[17] Polyphenols found in plants, particularly seeds, whole grains, and vegetables acting a role as antifeedants in the defence of seeds and plants against herbivores.

[18] A derivative of glucose comparable to cellulose – a primary component of cell walls in fungi.
the exoskeletons of arthropods such as crustaceans and insects, and the radulae, cephalopod beaks and gladii of molluscs.

[19] Valency is the measure of the combining capacity of an element with other atoms in the formation of chemical compounds or molecules.

[20] Chemical compounds that contain carbon-hydrogen bonds. Living things incorporate inorganic carbon compounds into organic compounds through photosynthesis.

I. CARBON DIOXIDE

Carbon dioxide is the most beneficial of all gas elements available to humanity.

It inflicts no harm or disadvantage on mankind. It forms just 0.041% of all atmospheric gasses.

Without it life would not exist.

It owes its paramount status to the following blessings it confers upon us all:-

- Plant synthesis of sugar from CO_2 and H_2O produces all oxygen - 21% of the atmosphere.

- It is the food of all plants and thus of all animals and human beings.

- With water vapour it maintains the Earth's surface heat at an average of 15^0C.

- Rising levels of CO_2 creates vast extensions of crop yields, forests and vegetation.

Historic concentrations

Throughout 99% of all geological periods since the appearance of multicellar organisms 600 million years ago atmospheric CO_2 density has exceeded the present very low levels by 5 to 8 orders of magnitude.

The following diagram describes the variations in concentrations of CO_2 and the oscillations of temperature during these geological periods. It is instructive in a number of respects and is referred in the text of this book in relation to the falsehoods about CO_2 disseminated over the past 30 years.

Figure 1

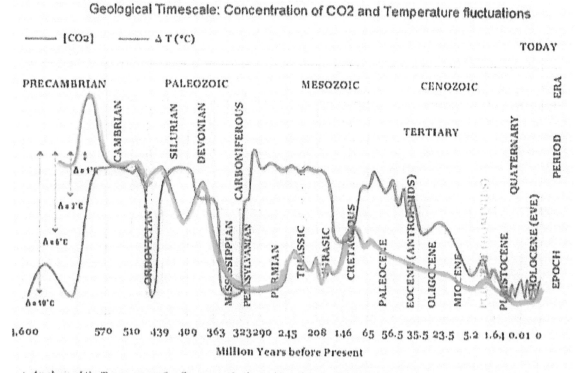

Geological Timescale: Concentration of CO2 and Temperature fluctuations

1- *Analysis of the Temperature Oscillations in Geological Eras by Dr. C. R. Scotese @ 2002. 2- Ruddiman, W. F. 2001. Earth's Climate: past and future. W. H. Freeman & Sons. New York, NY. 3- Mark Pagani et all, Marked Decline in Atmospheric Carbon Dioxide Concentrations During the Paleocene. Science; Vol. 309, No. 5734; pp. 600-603, 22 July 2005. Conclusion and Interpretation by Naal Nahle @ 2005, 2007.*

No polluting impact

We exhale well over 2 lbs of carbon dioxide each day as do all large animals. This represents approximately 5% of our breath. Modern fossil fuel power station emissions consist of 70% nitrogen, 5% uncombusted oxygen, 5% water vapour and 20% carbon dioxide.

However the CO_2 so emitted is at such temperature that despite being heavier than air it ascends well above the atmosphere immediately above the surface of the Earth (the troposphere) and takes effect in higher altitudes of the atmosphere to block incoming short wave solar radiation within the limited appropriate frequencies. It accordingly acts to some extent as a shade and a coolant.

Open combustion of poor quality carbon fuels produces harmful substances. These include chemicals containing sulphur, chlorine and fluorine. In unventilated small enclosures combustion produces highly poisonous carbon monoxide. Sulphur dioxide chokes humans. It is the cause of acid rain and destroys the fabric of stone buildings. Soot and smoke create brown clouds in extreme cases causing lung disease and many forms of respiratory afflictions. Lack of sunshine in the smogs of London in the 19th century caused rickets in children due to vitamin D deficiency.

CO_2 has no part in any such pollution.

It is a colourless, odourless gas. It has a density in the Earth's atmosphere of just 0.0417% or 417ppm. Its density locally varies considerably during the day and night. In a crowded room its density could be over 2000 ppm. In bright sunshine and open fields it could fall to 250ppm by reason of draw down by plants through photosynthesis. Densities increase at night as most plants convert from photosynthesis to respiration so producing carbon dioxide and water.

Carbon Cycle: lifetime of CO_2 in atmosphere

Carbon informs all the forms of matter that are essential to human existence. It moves continuously through all the fabric, liquids and atmosphere of the Earth. Over millions of years this cycle has evolved to maintain an equilibrium between photosynthesis, respiration and natural combustion. As is demonstrated in Part 2 the Earth is able to maintain an average surface temperature of 15^{0}C by means of thermostatic and other restraints despite variations of CO_2 atmospheric density.

The hydrosphere – the totality of all bodies of water of the planet – is the largest reservoir for atmospheric CO_2 holding at least 50 times more carbon than the atmosphere[21]. On best estimates the atmosphere exchanges 90bn tons of carbon with the surface ocean. Vegetation, bacteria, fungi and single cell creatures exchange 100bn tons. 48% of human emissions of CO_2 have been shown to be absorbed by the oceans[22] and 25% naturally sequestered by soils[23].

An important factor in determining the volume of atmospheric CO_2 is the period for which fossil fuel atmospheric CO_2 molecules remain in the atmosphere until they are 'scrubbed' as described above.

The lifetime of atmospheric CO_2 may be calculated by measuring the amount of C_{12}, C_{13} and C_{14}[24] in the gas. Further corroboration is found by measuring the inert gas radon 6% (Rn^{222}), CO_2 solubility and by further carbon isotope calculations.[25] 37 studies applying various of these tests and calculations show that the average lifetime of CO_2 in the atmosphere is approximately 5 years. A former IPCC Chairman and promoter of the hypothesis of global warming due to human CO_2 emissions has affirmed that such was indeed the case.[26] The IPCC models as to lifetime duration of atmospheric CO_2 are not founded on any form of carbon isotope evidence.

---

[21] Houghton RA 2007 Balancing the global carbon budget *Annual Review of Earth and Planetary Science* 25. pp313 – 347.

[22] Houghton RA Op cit at page 319 section 3.1.3.

[23] Professor Plimer Op cit p413 citing Lal R 2003 *Global potential of global carbon sequestration to mitigate greenhouse effect*. Critical Review of Plant Sciences 35. Pp151 – 184.

[24] C12 and C13 occur naturally and are stable. C14 is a radionuclide decaying with a half-life of about 5,730 years.

[25] *Heaven and Earth Global Warming the Missing Science*. Professor Ian Plimer 2009 Connor Court Publishing at p 415.

[26] Bolin B et al *Changes in the carbon dioxide content of the atmosphere and sea due to fossil fuel combustion* 1959.

A study published in 2009[27] found that both radioactive and stable carbon isotopes had revealed that CO_2 residence time in the atmosphere was approximately 5 years. This has the consequence that CO_2 is being taken out of the atmospheric reservoir with approximately 135 gigatonnes (about 18%) being exchanged each year. It also confirmed that only 4% of atmospheric CO_2 was accounted for by fossil fuel combustion by humans. That proportion is now 5% (see Section III page 22).

Sources of CO_2

The ultimate source of CO_2 is the lower crust of the Earth and its mantle which have released it by volcanic activity, tectonic ruptures and earthquakes since the formation of the planet and which continue today. There are more than 10,000 earthquakes each year. The reservoirs of CO_2 deep in the Earth far exceed any of the surface reservoirs of the gas.[28]

The oceans release more than 100bn tons of CO_2 as a consequence of decline in solubility with increasing temperature. Figure 2 shows change of global atmospheric CO_2 concentration (green), sea surface temperature (blue) and surface air temperature (red dotted) to 9 February 2022.[29] At least 56% of atmospheric CO_2 is given off in this way by the oceans.

Figure 2

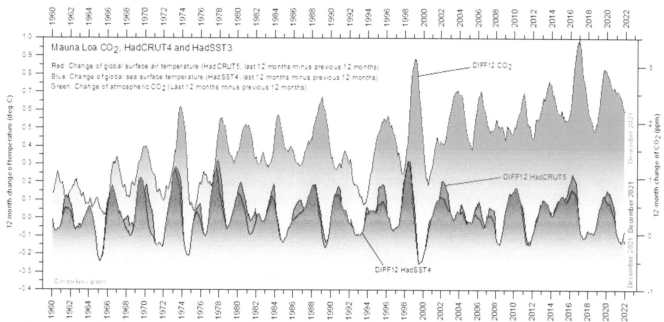

Humans, animals, microorganisms and plants together emit enormous volumes of CO_2 as a consequence of the process of respiration. 38% of atmospheric CO_2 is emitted by this means amounting to 71bn tons. No more than 5% of CO_2 in the air is the consequence of human activity.

Gasses of the atmosphere

The principal gasses in the atmosphere are nitrogen (N_2) at 78%, Oxygen (O_2) at 21% and Argon (Ar) at 0.93%. None of these impede the transfer of heat from the sun. The remaining gasses are known as trace gasses. These delay the escape of heat to space of 6% of solar heat re-radiated by the surface of the Earth. Of these gasses water vapour (H_2O) comprises 95%, CO_2 4.97%, methane (CH_4) 0.000175% and a minute volume of nitrous oxide . Ozone (O_3) forms 0.00006% of the atmosphere though in its principal concentrations in the stratosphere at 32 km its density increases to 0.0015%.

[27] Professor T V Segalstad, *Carbon cycle modelling and the residence time of natural and anthropogenic atmospheric CO^2* 2009 Environmental Science

[28] Professor Plimer Op cit p423

[29] Professor Ole Humlum Climate4U *Atmospheric carbon dioxide {CO_2}.*

Figure 1 above (page 13) charts the variations of temperature of the Earth (red) in relation to variations of density of CO_2 (blue) over the 550m years since the emergence of multicellular life. It demonstrates that there is no correlation between temperature and CO_2 over this period. Figure 3 sets out various charts of density of CO_2 during these ages.

Figure 3

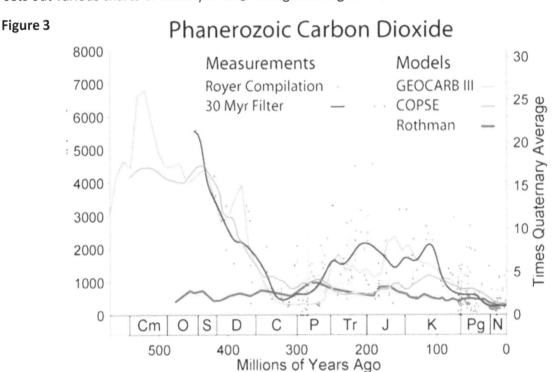

The Cambrian period 550m years ago saw the diversification of living creatures into complex organisms comprising almost all basic animal forms known today including chordates, to which vertebrates, animals with backbones such as humans, belong. At the opening of that era the CO_2 concentration in the atmosphere was 6,600 parts per million by volume (ppm). The vast draw down of CO_2 by organisms in the formation of calcium carbonate body structures and of planetary vegetation through photosynthesis resulted in the steep decline in this density shown in Figure 3.

In the Devonian period CO_2 levels were 3,500 ppm. In the later Devonian period and in the Carboniferous period concentrations fell to approximately 400/500ppm. The glaciation of 160m years spanning the late Carboniferous and early Permian periods 360/230 million years ago (mya) reduced temperatures to levels well below today and CO_2 concentrations fell to 200ppm[30].

CO_2 density increased very gradually over 100m years reaching maximum further concentration during the late Triassic period 240 – 180mya of approx 2,500 ppm and again in the Cretaceous period 125mya but then declining to approx 500ppm in the mid-Miocene epoch 15mya.

During the past 5m years it declined to 180/190ppm and remained at that level for the short period 20,000 -18,000 years ago[31]. That is the lowest concentration of atmospheric CO_2 to have occurred during 400m years of evolution of land plants[32]. Levels gradually rose to 280 ppm by 1890.

For 545 million years out of the past 550 million years (99.1%) since the explosion of complex life on our planet CO_2 levels in the atmosphere have exceeded the current level of 417ppm by at least 6 times (Triassic, late Jurassic and Cretaceous), 8 times (Devonian) and 16 times (Cambrian).

---

[30] *Plant responses to low CO₂ of the Past*. Gerhart M. and Ward J.K. New Phytologist (2010) 188 674 – 695.

[31] Gerhart M and Ward J.K Op cit p 675.

[32] Berner R.A *The long-term carbon cycle, fossil fuels and atmosphere composition* Nature 426: 323-326.

CO₂ concentrations: 1800 – 1959

The hypothesis of the IPCC that human combusted fossil fuel emissions are causing and will cause dangerous warming of the Earth's atmosphere depends on the claim that the rising concentrations of CO_2 since 1890 pre-industrial levels are unprecedented.

The assumptions made by the IPCC as to the 1890 concentrations of CO_2 are open to question.

Prior to 1959 when the infra red spectroscopic method of measuring CO_2 concentrations was adopted at the Mauna Loa (Hawaii) station the established basis of measurement was the Pettenkoffer method of chemical analysis of the air.

Measurements from 1812 and 1961 by this method had an error factor of less than 3%[33]. Average CO_2 concentration measured directly from the air in the 19th century was 315 – 331ppm[34]. Between 1812 and 1961 over 90,000 measurements of CO_2 density were made by chemical analysis[35]. These showed considerable variation with peaks in 1825, 1857 and 1942. Atmospheric content in 1942 was measured at 400ppm just at the point following the end of the warming period 1910 – 1940 (see Figure 31) – a level that it only again attained in 2018.

With the rise in surface temperature of the oceans a net increase in atmospheric CO_2 density would result by reason of diminished solubility. Figure 2 illustrates the correlation between rise in sea surface temperature and CO_2 release into the atmosphere.

Accordingly the process of release of CO_2 quite independent of human intervention as a consequence of declining solubility in the oceans with rise in temperature cannot be discounted – see Section II page 15 above.

In the 1980s ice core data began to replace measurement taken directly from the air. However evidence given to US Congress[36] has disputed whether ice core measurements have the degree of precision required to distinguish between concentrations with certainty.

Studies of stomatal frequency which in turn are related to intensity of CO_2 density reveal levels of between 333ppm and 348 ppm in the period of 9,600 – 9,400 years ago. Compression in deep ice converts gasses into solid gas hydrates (known as clathrates). However the process of drilling ice cores results in explosive decompression and escape of gas into the drilling fluid. This results in depletion of trapped CO_2.

Moreover even data from shallow ice cores, which are relied on by the IPCC as evidence of rapid acceleration of CO_2 density, reveal higher base densities at the start of the pre-industrial era. Ice deposited in 1890 at a depth of 68 metres had a concentration of 328ppm far higher relatively than the 290ppm ascribed to it by the IPCC hypothesis.

It is far from settled that there has been a dramatic and alarming increase in CO_2 density from a steady level of 270/280ppm prevailing for many thousands of years. Not only does it appear that there is a higher base level for the pre-industrial density of the order of 300ppm but other factors than human combustion of fossil fuels need to be taken into account.

It is not suggested that these factors displace fossil fuel combustion as a major contributor to increased density. But that they do contribute is certain though the extent is uncertain.

---

[33] Plimer Op cit p416 et seq.

[34] Plimer Op cit p 417.

[35] *180 Years accurate CO2 - Gas analysis of Air by Chemical Methods* Dipl. Biol. Ernst-Georg Beck, Biology and Bio-Technology Professor at the Merian-Schule Freiburg. 2008 21st Century Science and Technology pp 41 – 51

[36] Evidence of Professor Zbugniew Jaworowski to US Senate Committee on Commerce Science and Transportation March 2004.

No acidification of the oceans

When CO_2 is dissolved in seawater it forms weak carbonic acid. However this is neutralised by conversion to bicarbonate by reactions with dissolved carbonate and borate in water and with calcium carbonate sediment on the ocean floor. Calcium in seawater binds dissolved CO_2 into insoluble carbonates of calcium in shells, coral reefs and mineral precipitates. Furthermore, the oceans have an excess of calcium. They are saturated with calcium carbonate to a depth of 4.8km so that any further CO_2 precipitates cal- cium carbonate which ultimately forms limestone deposits.

Coral reefs are expanding[37] and contracting as they have for millions of years. The current scare is that the oceans are being made acid as a result of the minute increase (5% of 0.041%) in atmospheric CO_2 caused by human emissions of fossil fuels. Some 85% of the Earth's volcanoes are submarine and emit colossal volumes of CO_2 which is dissolved in the cold of the deep ocean.

Ocean acidity is measured as pH. It is now between pH 7.9 – 8.2. Neutral is pH 7. Thus the oceans are alkaline. To acidify oceans at a level of pH6 ten times more acid is needed than for pH7. To acidify sea-water from 8.2pH to pH6 vast amounts of acid are necessary.

It is alleged that acidification due to CO_2 results in loss of calcium carbonate used to create skeletons including corals. However the geological record shows that shells do not dissolve even at 16 times CO_2 density when shell and skeletal formation began.

Acid which is indeed harmful is formed from hydrogen sulphide and sulphur dioxide which oxidise to sulphuric acid which is catastrophic for fish.

It is now believed that the dinosaur extinction event of 65 – 70million years ago was due to the Deccan Traps flow of basalt. These created one of the largest volcanic features on Earth. It crops out over 500,000 sq. km of the west-central Indian subcontinent. The trap complex is predominantly composed of multiple layers of tholeiitic flood basalt. The thickness varies from more than 2000m in the Western Ghats to over 1000m in the eastern part of the province. The clouds of sulphuric acid created by this catastrophe not only destroyed organic life directly but also obscured sunlight and heat so inhibiting photosynthesis.

At the level of the ocean floor the reaction of the vast sheets of volcanic basalt and seawater renders seawater more alkaline by removing CO_2 from seawater to form carbonates. Basalt is a highly reactive rock particularly when fractured. In addition marine micro-organisms that consume CO_2 increase alkalinity and it is just such organisms that flourish with rising CO_2 concentrations. They account for up to 75% of photosynthetic conversion of CO_2.

These reactions control the alkaline and acid balance of the oceans.

There have been vast changes in CO_2 density since the Cambrian era which heralded the arrival of multicellular predatory creatures. CO_2 density in the Cambrian era was 14-16 times the concentration of today. Yet the oceans have not become acid. Fossilised shells, algal reefs, and coral reefs reveal that ocean alkalinity was maintained even at far higher temperatures.

There is a balance between mineral and biological processes that has been maintained over hundreds of millions of years. The very same water rock chemical reactions that keep the oceans saline also keep them alkaline. If the oceans were becoming acid they would become less saline. This has not happened.[38]

The absurd contention that acid oceans are dissolving shells is utterly false.

---

[37] Dr Paul Kench Coastal Geomorphologist University of Auckland reported on Australian ABS the expansion of coral atolls in the Marshall Islands, Kiribati and Maldives archipelago by 8%: wattsupwiththat.com 10th January 2021.
[38] Plimer Op cit p 337

Increased concentrations of CO_2 enhance shell formation. Such was the vertebrate explosion of the Cambrian period which saw the development of myriad marine creatures with calcium carbonate shells. The geological record shows that dissolution of shells did not occur.

Myths about bleaching of coral reefs

A common false assertion is repeatedly made that increase in CO2 density in the atmosphere is causing destruction of coral reefs by bleaching[39]. It is extraordinary that any credit at all is given to this falsely alarming statement. Bleaching occurs when coral polyps eject phytoplankton during warmer of colder conditions. It is the plankton that give coral its colours varying according to the plankton ingested. Thus the polyps and coral structure made of calcium carbonate lose colour and appear white.

For millions of years CO_2 density and temperature have been at levels far higher than today. Corals appeared as solitary forms in the fossil record more than 400 million years ago. They evolved into reef-building forms over the last 25 million years.

Pollution and run off from land have had a considerable adverse impact on coral reefs. In areas of the oceans which have had no such impacts there are no signs of decline due to alleged acidification[40].

Corals recover[41] rapidly from bleaching[42]. The 2016 bleaching was almost certainly the result of the sharp rise in global temperature caused by the El Nino[43] event 2015/6. The 2021/22 bleaching was caused by the temperature spike of the major La Nina[44] event of those years. See Figure 4 diagrams illustrating the La Nina and El Nino effects.

Bleaching has been a feature of coral reefs for millions of years and at times of vastly greater concentrations of CO_2 and higher temperatures.

La Nina effect

Sudden changes in sea surface temperature in cloud free skies due to the La Nina and the El Nino effects are the paramount causes of bleaching.

It has now been established that the La Nina oscillation causes extensive bleaching. The 2021/2022 La Nina has created unusually warm ocean temperatures despite its cooling effects elsewhere in the Pacific. Sea surface temperatures over the Australian summer remained above average in many parts of the Reef with rises of up to 4°C.

La Nina, like El Nino, is a weather pattern that can occur in the Pacific Ocean every few years. In a normal year, winds along the equator push warm water westward. Warm water at the surface of the ocean blows from South America to Indonesia. As the warm water moves west, cold water from the deep ocean moving to the coast of South and Central America rises up to the surface.

---

[39] Coral bleaching is the process whereby corals become white due to various stressors, such as changes in temperature, light, or nutrients. Bleaching occurs when coral polyps expel the algae that live inside their tissue, causing the coral to turn white.

[40] Woods Hole Oceanographic Institution 27th August 2020.

[41] See article "*Marvellous Resilient Coral*" 5 October 2019 wattsupwiththat.com . See also the *Phoenix effect* of coral recovery described by Dave Krupp a coral researcher in Hawaii who works with *Fungia scutaria*. Bleaching does not mean death. 2016 bleaching of the coral in the Coral Sea Marine Park did not result in any significant loss of coral cover.

[42] The process of bleaching occurs when coral expel algae on which it depends.

[43] The El Nino Southern Oscillation {ENSO} is a periodic shift of the ocean-atmosphere system in the tropical Pacific that impacts weather around the world. It happens every 3-7 years and typically lasts nine months to two years. It is associated with floods, droughts, and other global disturbances.

[44] La Nina is a weather pattern that occurs in the Pacific Ocean. In this pattern, strong winds blow warm water at the ocean's surface from South America to Indonesia.

Figure 4

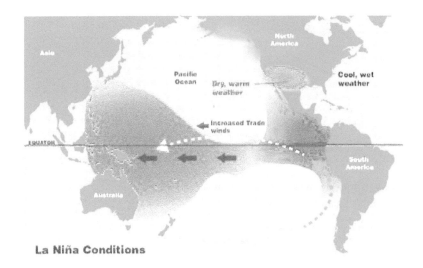

La Niña Conditions

El Nino effect

The 1997/1998 El Niño caused a most severe coral bleaching event, resulting in the loss of 16 % of the world's coral reefs. Mortality was particularly severe in French Polynesia, where unprecedented decease of massive Porites was observed in lagoonal sites.

However recovery was rapid and abundant. Surveys[45] revealed an abundance of massive Porites[46] colonies rising from shallow lagoonal floors. The relative cover of recently dead skeleton coral declined from 42.8 % in 1998 to zero in 2013. The proportion of Porites dominated by living tissue increased from 34.9 % in 1998 to 73.9 % in 2013 with recovery of dead skeleton to living tissue. Such rapid post-bleaching recovery resulted from remarkable self-regeneration whereby remnant patches of tissue that survived the 1997/1998 event regenerated and rapidly overgrew adjacent dead skeleton.

The severe 2014/2016 El Nino caused significant bleaching but recovery was just as it had occurred after the 1997/1998 event. It will recover just as rapidly after the 2021/22 event.

SUMMARY

CO_2 is the source of food of all plants and so of animals and human beings. With water vapour it maintains the Earth's surface heat at an average of 15⁰C. Rising CO_2 creates vast extensions of crop yields, forests and vegetation. From CO_2 we derive all the oxygen we breathe. It forms just 0.041% of all atmospheric gasses. It is not a pollutant.

---

45 *Porites and the Phoenix effect: Unprecedented recovery after a mass coral bleaching event at Rangiroa Atoll, French Polynesia* George Roff, Sonia Bejara et al June 2014 Marine Biology 161(6):1385-1393 DOI:10.1007/s00227-014-2426-6. 46 *Corals of the genus Porites create a calcium carbonate exoskeleton resembling human bone. Porites, particularly Porites lutea, often form microatolls.*

PART 2

Blind belief in authority is the enemy of truth

Albert Einstein

III.   GREENHOUSE EFFECT: BASIC CONCEPTS

The greenhouse effect is the warming of molecules of water vapour and CO_2 due to oscillations caused by electromagnetic infra red radiation from the Earth's surface acting upon the molecular dipole moments (see Section V). These result in processes of absorption and emission of energy which delay the escape of heat to space. Methane, nitrous oxide and ozone also have this effect but to a very limited extent. The greenhouse effect keeps the Earth's temperature at an average of 15^0C. This is $30/32^0C$ higher than it would otherwise be. It renders the Earth habitable.

The greenhouse effect also initiates the rise of such energy by convection to higher altitudes from where it is radiated to space so allowing cold air to descend in the cycle of convection to cool the lower atmosphere.

Wavelength and Frequency

Wavelength and frequency are critical to the extent to which of electromagnetic infra red radiation creates the greenhouse effect.

Wavelength is the distance between two close oscillation points of a wave within phase with each other. Frequency is the number of oscillations of a wave within a given width.

Figure 5

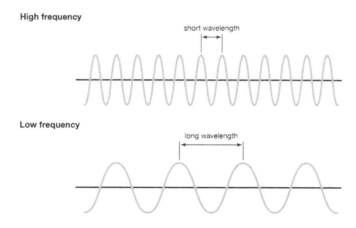

Wavelength and frequency are inversely proportional to each other. The wave with the greatest frequency has the shortest wavelength. The more heat that is radiated the shorter the wavelength and the higher the frequency.

As is described in Section VII the warmth created by the greenhouse effect is radiated in all directions including upwards through the troposphere by the process of convection.

It does not accumulate nor is it trapped in the lower atmosphere.

Garden greenhouse

Solar radiation is emitted at very short wavelengths. It is accordingly able to pass freely through the glass of a garden greenhouse. However the re-radiation of such energy from the floor, soil and plants in the greenhouse is at much longer wavelengths and lower frequencies. At over 4 microns (1/1000mm) such re-radiated heat is indeed trapped in a garden greenhouse. It cannot escape through convection[47]. It can only escape to a limited extent through conduction[48] through the glass itself. That is very limited indeed. As soon as ventilators are opened heat is convected to the air.

No heat trap or blanket

It is often said that CO_2 acts as a trap in which heat cannot escape. This is falsely alarming[49].

As is set out in Section VII, so far from acting as a 'trap' greenhouse gasses create the process of convection that transfers heat 15/20km to the top of the lower atmosphere. In so doing heat is lost at the rate of 9.7^0C every km of altitude. At higher altitudes the energy is radiated to space and cold air descends to cool the atmosphere at its base.

There is no layer of greenhouse gasses. There is no blanket or trap.

CO_2 is diffused at consistent concentrations throughout the atmosphere as high as 84km. Nitrogen (78%) and oxygen (21%) form 99% of the atmosphere – CO_2 forms just 0.0417%.

There are over 20 times more molecules of H_2O than CO_2 close to the surface of the Earth where the greenhouse effect occurs. Water vapour forms 95% of all greenhouse gasses. CO_2 forms 4.87%. It is responsible for approximately 20% (18% – 22%) of the greenhouse effect.

Human emissions of CO_2 from fossil fuel combustion amount to approximately 38bn tons each year. Plants and animals (including humans) emit CO_2 when they respire, decay or burn amounting to 440bn tons a year . The oceans release some 330bn tons a year.

Accordingly the contribution of CO_2 from fossil fuel emissions is just 5%.

Key factors limiting warming

There are 6 paramount factors that govern the effect that the presence of CO_2 in the atmosphere has upon the temperature of the Earth.

- The extent of electromagnetic solar infra red energy re-radiated by Earth's surface.

- The limits on the means of absorption of energy by greenhouse gas molecules.

- The limited range of the electromagnetic absorption frequency bands.

- The thermostatic constraints on Earth's surface temperature.

- The convective rise of energy, radiation to space and cooling of atmosphere.

- The saturation limits on any further absorption by CO_2 of radiated energy.

Of these limitations the saturation of the absorption bands of radiation of 14 – 16 microns is of over-whelming importance.

Each of these phenomena requires examination.

---

[47] Motion of air caused by thermal expansion and buoyancy forces that result from atmospheric density variations due to variations of thermal temperature.

[48] Transfer of internal energy by microscopic collisions of particles and movement of electrons within a body.

[49] The British Prime Minister absurdly described the greenhouse effect at the Climate Conference at Glasgow in November 2021 as a "tea cosy".

II. SUN'S ENERGY AND THE EARTH

The sun emits radiation in short wave frequencies. On reaching the atmosphere the radiated solar energy is 1361 Watts per m^2. It consists of ultraviolet, visible light and infra red radiation.

Loss of solar incoming radiation

52% of such energy does not reach the surface of the Earth at all.

Of the incoming solar energy 29% is reflected back by clouds, ice and snow or scattered by high aerosols[50].

A further 23% is blocked by absorption in the higher atmosphere by dust, water vapor, clouds and ozone and at lower altitudes by water vapour. CO_2 is an effective absorber of solar incoming radiation in the 2.7 and 4.4 micron frequency bands but the intensity of such radiation is low at these frequencies.

In the stratosphere ozone (O_3) blocks ultra violet (UV)-C and most of the sunburn-producing UV-B band in longer wavelengths than UV-C. UV-A is closest to visible light and most reaches the surface.

Figure 6

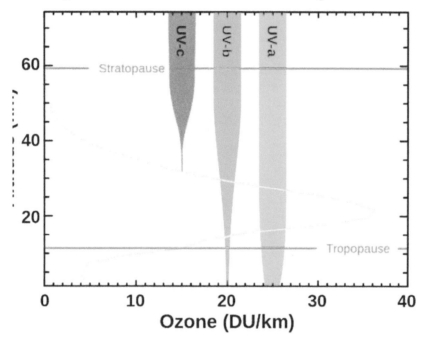

The absorption and emission of such radiation in the higher stratosphere does not have any greenhouse effect at all in the lower atmosphere (troposphere}.

Transfer of radiation from Earth's surface

Only **48%** of the Sun's energy reaches the surface of the Earth.

This is then transferred by 3 processes.

5% is transmitted by convection through molecular contact with all other molecules including nitrogen (N_2} and oxygen (O_2} with the warm surface. It rises through the lower troposphere by convection and is redistributed in the cooler air through the rest of the troposphere.

---

[50] An aerosol is a suspension of fine particles or droplets in air or other gas. They also form necessary seeds for cloud formation. Natural aerosols are fog or mist, dust, forest exudates, and geyser steam. Examples of human emitted aerosols are particulate pollutants, ash and smoke. Their impact on climate is not fully understood.

25% is transferred by evaporation or the latent heat vaporisation of the oceans and lakes. These together comprise 71% of Earth surface. Evaporated water vapour reaches the lower troposphere where it forms droplets and is distributed to the cooler regions of the atmosphere.

Radiation is the third means of transfer of energy. It is infra red radiation emitted back from the surface of the Earth that accounts for the remaining 18% of solar energy that reaches it.

12% of such energy is radiated direct into space. This occurs through windows or gaps in the frequency bands of the electromagnetic radiation spectrum in which no energy is absorbed by greenhouse gasses. The main atmospheric window is between wavelengths of 8 and 13 microns.

6% of the radiation emitted by the surface is absorbed mainly by water vapour molecules but some by CO_2. It is immediately re-emitted and absorbed. In the first 100m of altitude 75% of radiation is absorbed. At 200m almost all infra red surface radiation is fully absorbed to the limited extent that absorption is possible within the bands of the absorption frequencies and limits of quanta of energy transferred.

It makes its way through the lower atmosphere principally by convection. Temperature decreases with declining atmospheric pressure in the troposphere from the Earth's surface to the junction with the stratosphere (tropopause) at a rate of 9.7 C^0 in dry atmosphere and 6.5C^0 per km in a moist atmosphere – these are known as the lapse rates[51]. It then radiates to space.

Figure 7 shows the function of solar panels absorbing surface insolation[52]. The grey area is the total light produced from the sun that actually reaches the surface of the Earth. The coloured spectrum is the solar radiation at sea level. The gaps represent light absorption and conversion into heat by greenhouse gasses. The light blue area is the radiation that silicone cells convert into electricity

Figure 7

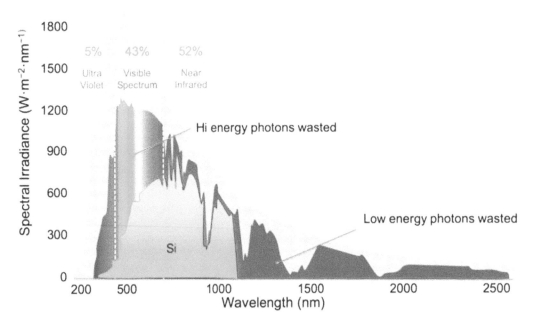

SUMMARY

Only 6% of solar energy re-radiates from the surface to be absorbed by greenhouse gasses. Human emissions form 5% of total CO_2 emissions into the atmosphere. CO_2 accounts for 18%- 22% of the greenhouse effect. Water vapour accounts for 80% - 75%.

---

[51] This is a form of convection created by greenhouse gasses. It is explained at Section VII.

[52] The amount of downward solar radiation energy incident on a plane surface.

V.   CO₂ ABSORPTION OF SURFACE HEAT

Absorption of electromagnetic radiation from the surface of the Earth is how matter – typically electrons in atoms – takes up the energy of a photon so transforming electromagnetic energy into internal energy of the absorber. The process of energy transfer to greenhouse gas molecules is by electromagnetic radiation exciting the dipole moment of the molecules of H_2O and CO_2. Other molecules have negligible effect.

Radiation itself has relatively little heat capacity. It is molecules of the greenhouse gasses – predominantly water vapour – that account for virtually all of atmospheric heat.

Radiation heat transfer is the energy that is emitted by matter in the form of photons or electromagnetic waves. It does not require an intervening medium. All bodies radiate energy in the form of photons or quanta of electromagnetic energy. Photons are without mass and move in random directions. Electromagnetic waves appear in nature over an unlimited range of wavelengths. Radiation in the 0.1 to 100 micron frequencies is in the form of thermal radiation. This includes all visible light and infra red radiation and some ultraviolet radiation. All bodies above absolute zero emit radiation over wide frequencies. A 'black body' is an idealised notional body which absorbs all incident radiation without interference or impediment.

Oscillatory absorption of energy

The capacity of a molecule to interact with electromagnetic energy is governed by the existence of what is known as a dipole moment for that molecule. Dipole moments exist if a molecule has spatial separation of the centre of a negative electron charge and the centre of a positive nuclear charge. It is the product of that separation and the magnitude of the positive charge.

For nitrogen (78%) and oxygen (21%) which comprise 99% of the atmosphere both charges are at the centre of the molecule and of its mass. Thus there is no separation and a zero dipole moment.

The following diagrams show CO_2 to the left H2O to the right. CO_2 is a linear triatomic molecule. H_2O is a triatomic tetrahedral shape – its molecular shape is bent with an H-O-H angle of 104.5°.

Figure 8

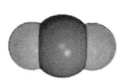   

The water vapour molecule is far more effective in absorbing infra red radiation than any of the other greenhouse gasses. At 20 times the molecular concentration of CO_2 in the lower troposphere, where the absorption of radiation occurs, H_2O dominates CO_2 and other greenhouse gasses in the frequency bands that it shares with them. It has many more spectrum lines and frequencies for absorption and a perfect form of structure for dipole moment excitation.

In the unexcited state the CO_2 molecule, being linear, does not have a dipole moment as the centres of negative and positive charge each coincide with the centre of symmetry. However a CO_2 molecule can bend and vibrate upon collision with another molecule. At the lowest level of the atmosphere each molecule experiences a collision at a rate of a billion collisions a second. This induces the molecule to oscillate by bending vibration and in so doing it has a dipole moment from the point of the centre. There is another form of dipole vibrational moment but the bending mode is the most effective form of this vibration mode.

There is a further form of oscillation excitation. This comprises the rotation of the molecule. Molecules in a state of vibration do not readily emit or absorb radiation along the axis of the vibration. Most radiation is emitted at right angles to the axis. For that reason the CO_2 vibrational bending mode is very effective at 15 microns frequency or 667.4 centimetre wavelength but it is not of itself able to extend absorption to other frequencies. It is by means of rotation of the molecule that wider frequencies become available in the form of sidebands. These are added to the vibrational frequency. The sideband with the lower frequency is known as the P branch – the higher is known as the R branch.

These vibrating and rotating electric dipole moments of oscillation are the efficient molecular antennas for absorbing and emitting electromagnetic radiation. As the electromagnetic wave passes the molecule its electric field will interact and excite changes in the molecule dipole moment.

It is essential that the energy contained in the electromagnetic photon is precisely as needed to put the molecule in the rotational or vibrational mode. Energy transfer can only be done in Quanta (Quanti) steps. The energy in the photon must be exactly equal to the energy required to prompt the molecule to oscillate with vibration or rotation or both. The energy needed to get to the next mode of rotation or vibration have to be identical to the energy within the photon. When that happens the energy of the photon will be absorbed, the photon will disappear and the energy will be contained in the molecule.

This is the key to the phenomenon of the greenhouse effect and the absorption of surface infra red radiation by water vapour and carbon dioxide molecules. It requires a brief explanation.

Planck's Black Body radiation spectrum curve

Earth's surface radiation excites oscillations in a molecule through a change in its dipole moment. The radiation is emitted or absorbed due to changing rotational-vibrational movements. Infrared spectroscopy enables examination of absorption and transmission of photons in the infrared range.

Until 1900 physics was confronted by a seemingly insoluble problem in the realm of thermal radiation. It was known that the shorter the frequencies of radiation from a radiated body the greater the intensity of the radiation. However if taken to its logical extent this meant that radiation intensity would ultimately be infinite as seen with the right hand black curve in Figure 9.

Figure 9

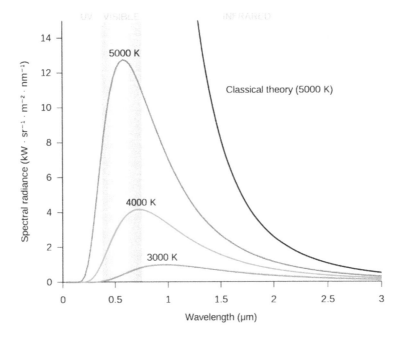

In 1900 Max Planck (1858-1947) empirically derived a formula for the observed spectrum of frequencies of radiation. He assumed a hypothetical electrically charged oscillator in a cavity that contained black body radiation[53] could only change its energy in a minimal increment that was proportional to the frequency of its associated electromagnetic wave. He was able to calculate the proportionality 'constant' from the experimental measurements.

It was thus possible for diagrammatic curves to be established showing intensity of radiation from a black body with a family of curves for different temperatures. In particular a curve was established for radiative heat intensity from a surface at frequencies of 0 – 2200 centimetres at the average temperature of the Earth of 15.5°C for a transparent atmosphere with no greenhouse gasses.

At the core of Planck's new derivation was the supposition, now known as the Planck postulate, that electromagnetic energy could be emitted only in quantised form, in other words, the energy could only be a multiple of an elementary unit:

$E = hv$

Where E is energy, h is Planck's constant, and v is the frequency of the radiation. Physicists now call these quanta photons and a photon of a particular frequency will have its own specific and unique energy. The total energy at that frequency is then equal to **hv** multiplied by the number of photons at that frequency.

Thus there has to be a minimum and precise level of energy capable of being absorbed at any particular wavelength or frequency. No absorption can otherwise occur.

The following is a short summary of how this affects energy absorption in the two principal forms of molecular oscillation under electromagnetic radiation.

Molecular Vibrational and Rotational Modes

There are various energy levels for the vibrational mode. To get from the base ground state to the 1st excited mode to the 2nd excited mode to the 3rd excited mode and so on the difference in energy required is exactly the same namely 1/2hv, 3/2 hv, 5/2 hv, 7/2 hv and so on.

The difference in energy level is quantised. The only way in which the atom can get to the next vibrational state is to add exactly the amount of energy required to go from one vibrational state to the next.

In the rotational mode the energy required to go in quantum from one level to the next level by quantum jumps is by 2x, 4x, 6x, 8x, 12x and so on. Thus there exponential increases of energy are required to raise levels.

The only way energy can be increased is through quantum jumps which in the vibrational mode depend on the base mode frequency of the oscillator or in the rotational mode depend on the base energy in question.

The combination of the vibrational and rotational modes allows molecular aborption of energy over a greater number of frequencies within the absorption 14 – 16 micron bands.

---

[53] An idealised physical body that allows all incident radiation to pass into it, having no reflected energy, which internally absorbs all the incident radiation with no energy transmitted through the body.

VI. ABSORPTION FREQUENCIES

Available frequencies

It has been noted that a maximum of 6% of solar energy is re-radiated from the surface of the Earth to be absorbed by greenhouse gasses. CO_2 absorbs approximately 18% – 22% of this thermal energy comprising 1.08% – 1.32% of the total.

That is because the extent to which CO_2 is able as a matter of physics to absorb such radiation is confined to a limited band of electromagnetic frequencies as well as being determined in quanta[54].

Figure 10

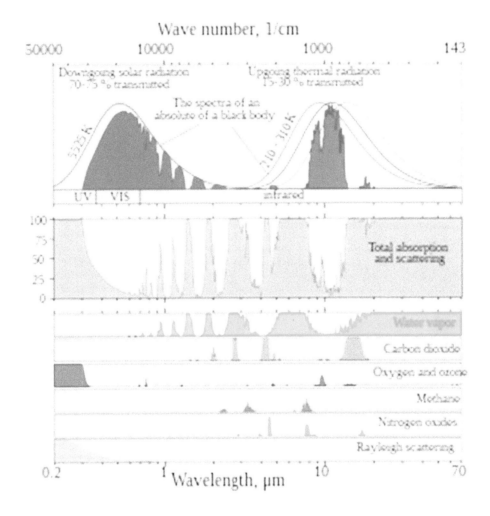

The most effective absorption by CO_2 occurs in the 14 to 16 micron bands with the maximum being at 15 microns or 667.4 cm at which the bending mode of vibration of the CO_2 molecule is at maximum oscillation. There is a strong absorption capacity at 2.7 microns and 4.257 microns but these are low points of the radiation spectrum with consequent little absorption. Moreover there is total overlap with H_2O at 2.7 microns accounting for all absorption of the constricted radiation in that waveband.

---

[54] A quantum (plural quanta) is the minimum amount of any physical entity (physical property) involved in an interaction. This means that the magnitude of the physical property can take on only discrete values consisting of integer multiples of one quantum. A photon is a single quantum of electromagnetic radiation.

Figure 10 also shows how the small absorption bands of 1.4, 1.6 and 2.0 are each taken up by direct 'downgoing' solar radiation, not by 'upgoing' re-radiation from the surface. They are in any case at the weakest points of such radiation.

Dominance of water vapour

The overlap of greenhouse gasses with H_2O and with each other severely curtails the extent of theoretically possible absorption of radiation by each of them in the absence of overlap.

H_2O is a triangular molecule so that it has a strong dipole moment unlike CO_2. It has many more oscillatory modes not shared by CO_2 including rocking and twisting, with overtones[55] and combinations of greater variety.

The dominance of H_2O exerts a further strict limitation on the effectiveness of CO_2 to absorb radiation. In the 1 – 10-micron bands there is substantially full radiation absorption by H_2O save for the 4.257 micron band which is close to the minimum radiation of the Planck curve and thus of little significance. From 20 microns radiation is again fully absorbed by H_2O. Between 14 and 16 microns there is partial absorption by H_2O so that the 15-micron band is shared as to 65% by H_2O and 35% by CO_2.

The following diagram shows the dominion of H_2O over CO_2.

Figure 11

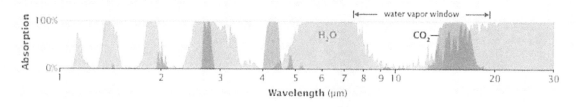

https://earthobservatory.nasa.gov/features/EnergyBalance

It will be seen from Figures 10 and 11 that there is a substantial window at between 8 and 13 microns in which surface infra red radiation escapes direct to space.

It follows that for the temperature of the Earth to be increased by the thermal resistance of CO_2 acting to slow down escape of infra red surface radiation to space an increase in unoccupied absorbing wave-length bands is required. No such bands exist.

SUMMARY

Radiated energy from the Earth's surface can only be absorbed by greenhouse gasses in quanta. Furthermore, such energy can only be absorbed within limited wave frequencies. The limits of effective CO_2 absorption are from 14 – 16 microns. All unabsorbed radiation outside these frequencies escapes to space through the atmospheric window of 8 – 13 microns.

---

[55] Overtone band is the spectral band that occurs in a vibrational spectrum of a molecule when the molecule makes a transition from the ground state (v=0) to the second excited state (v=2).

VII.   EARTH'S TEMPERATURE THERMOSTATS

The surface of the Earth has the benefit of two forms of thermostat operating to attenuate surface temperature. The physics of these thermostats are enshrined in two laws namely Stefan Bolzmann's law and Wiens displacement law. Each law concerns increase in heat energy in relation to radiation frequency. A diagram of these in conjunction is seen in Figure 12.

Earth's temperature at the surface is an average of 288K (Kelvin absolute temperature[56]) or 15°C. A hot oven is 500K or 226°C. Volcanic lavas range in temperature from about 1,000K or 726°C to 1,400K or 1,126°C. An electric current heats the filament of an incandescent light bulb typically to 2,000 – 3,300K (1,726°C – 3,026°C).

Figure 12

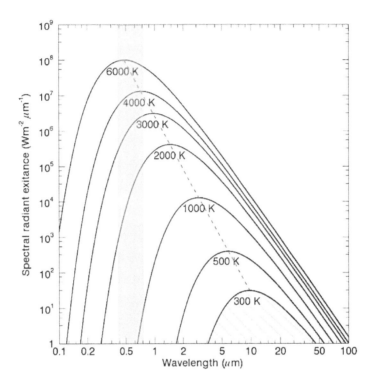

Stefan Boltzmann's law

This may be summarily stated as being the principle that the total intensity of energy radiated over all wavelengths increases as the temperature of a black body increases in proportion to the fourth power of the thermodynamic temperature.

Putting it in very simplistic terms the power or energy radiated by the surface is governed by the area of surface and by temperature to the power of 4.

A 20°C increase from -20°C to 0°C results in 35% greater heat energy radiation. A 40°C increase to +20C is 80% greater. A 60°C increase to +40C results in 134% greater radiation.

Radiation thus increases exponentially as temperature increases. This phenomenon acts as thermostat on the Earth's surface temperature since very small changes in temperature effect significant changes in energy being radiated into space.

---

[56] Kelvin temperature scale is a temperature scale having an absolute zero below which temperatures do not exist. Absolute zero, or 0°K, is the temperature at which molecular energy is a minimum, and it corresponds to a temperature of −273° C.

Wien's displacement law .

Wien's law states that there is an inverse relationship between wavelength and temperature such that the higher the temperature, the shorter or smaller the wavelength of the thermal radiation. Likewise the lower the temperature, the longer or larger the wavelength of the thermal radiation.

When temperature increases the peak of emitted radiation on the Planck curve (blackbody) moves to shorter wave length bands from 11.46 microns at -20° C to 9.27 microns at +40° C and it also increases in height.

However when temperature decreases the peak of emitted radiation (black body curve) moves back to longer wave length bands and so increases CO_2 absorption capability since the most effective bands serving CO_2 are between 14 – 16 microns.

The shift of peak radiation to shorter wavelengths with increased temperature has 2 consequences:

•   Much more radiation goes up to space through the radiation window of 8 – 13 microns by direct radiation to space: and

•   The CO_2 optimal band of 15 microns is absorbing much less radiation as the Planck curve declines sharply with the shift of the peak of the black body curve to shorter wavelengths.

Thus CO_2 is much more effective as a greenhouse gas at the Poles in cold conditions and much less effective at the equator. In this way temperature regulates the greenhouse effect.

Greenhouse gas convection cooling

The presence of greenhouse gasses in the lower atmosphere close to the surface of the Earth gives rise to the process of convection.

Greenhouse gasses create a form of thermal resistance of the atmosphere to the vertical flow of energy from the surface of the Earth heated by the sun. The warming of the molecules of H_2O and CO_2 creates thermal expansion of the air. This expansion of air in the diminishing atmospheric pressure above the surface of the Earth causes it to rise. The decrease in pressure causes it to cool. Atmospheric pressure at sea level is 10 tons per square metre. At the top of the troposphere it is approximately 2.7 tons.

It is the expansion with declining pressure that causes the loss of energy and thus loss of heat. However it must be understood that this process is adiabatic. That is to say it is a process that neither allows the heat to transfer inside air parcels[57] nor does it let the heat out. It is the very expansion that is the thermodynamic 'work' in the sense that energy is lost which is not replaced so resulting in loss of heat. As the gas is allowed to expand and the volume increases, the temperature falls as its internal energy decreases.

Temperature in the troposphere falls over 8/15 kilometres[58] from +15°C to -50°C. As air parcels rise by convection the expansion causes the loss of heat so that they cool and contract. There comes a point in the higher altitudes of 15km – 20km around the tropopause when the energy is then radiated to space and cold air sinks to complete the convection cycle. Being heavier than the surrounding air the air parcels sink and are replaced by parcels of warmer air rising from below. Figures 13 and 14 show such temperature changes and stages of convection and radiation.

---

[57] An abstract volume of air to which may be assigned any or all of the basic dynamic and thermodynamic properties of atmospheric air (such as temperature or humidity) so as to predict its movements according to the laws of physics.
[58] The troposphere varies in altitude from 8km at the poles and 15km at the equator.

Energy is thus transferred to the upper tropopause by the process of convection. Convection is the dominant process of heat transfer in troposphere. It is not done by thermal radiation since it is the very de- cline in temperature that inhibits thermal radiation. Above the tropopause the increase in temperature of the stratosphere, due to ozone absorption of solar ultra violet radiation, encourages radiation and it is by this means that greenhouse gasses release energy to space.

Figure 13

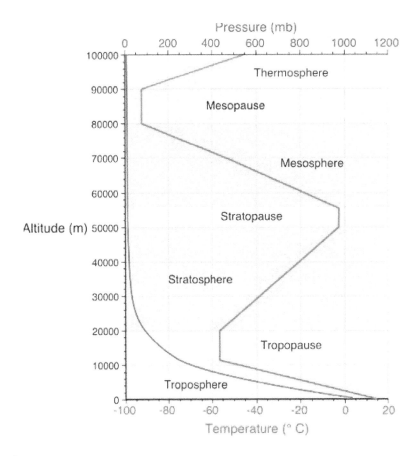

Adiabatic cooling lapse rates

The rate of decline in temperature with altitude is known as the lapse rate.

The rate of heat loss is affected by the moisture of the air. When water vapour saturates a rising air parcel some will condense and release latent heat. This process causes the parcel to cool more slowly than it would if it were not saturated. The moist adiabatic lapse rate varies considerably because the amount of water vapour in the air is highly variable. The greater the amount of vapour, the smaller the adiabatic lapse rate. This is of the order of 6.5°C per kilometre. As an air parcel rises and cools, it may eventually lose its moisture through condensation: its lapse rate then increases and approaches what is known as the dry adiabatic value or 9.8°C per kilometre.

The process of rising and sinking air parcels exchanges very little actual heat with the surrounding air. It simply carries the solar radiation absorbed by the surface to sufficiently high altitudes for it to be radiated to pace so cooling the upper atmosphere. [59]

The process of adiabatic cooling inhibits radiation. However it ceases when the air parcels reach isothermic[60] conditions in the lower stratosphere and so allows radiation direct to space.

---

[59] *Cooling of Atmosphere Due to CO$_2$ Emission.* G.V Chilingar et al Energy and Environment Laboratory, University of Southern California, Los Angeles USA. Institute of Oceanology of Russian Academy of Sciences, Moscow, Russia. Energy Sources, Part A [30]: 1-9, 2008
[60] Equal or constant temperature with respect to space.

Figure 14

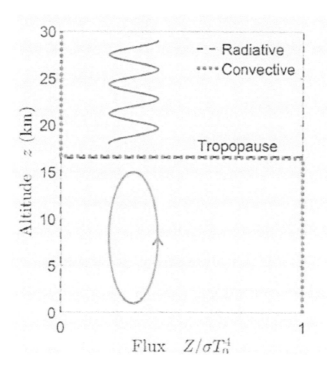

It is important to grasp that the role of greenhouse gasses is to maintain a balance of temperature.

The average surface temperature is at +15°C much higher than the radiation temperature of the Earth of -18°C. It is the greenhouse gasses that procure this effect.

However greenhouse gasses also initiate convection of the air in the troposphere rising adiabatically in declining temperature. It is this that results in transfer of solar energy absorbed by the greenhouse effect to be radiated and emitted in the tropopause and lower stratosphere where temperature is constant allowing cold air to descend and cool the lower atmosphere.

SUMMARY

Rise in surface temperature causes a shift of radiation to higher frequencies of radiation resulting in diminished absorption by CO_2 and increased escape to space. Infra red energy absorbed by CO_2 does not accumulate or form a barrier or blanket or a trap. It rises 15km – 20km by convection and is radiated to space above the troposphere allowing cold air to descend with the cycle of convection to cool the surface.

VIII. SATURATION

Limitations on absorption by CO_2 molecules

It has been demonstrated in this Part 2 that:

- 6% of incoming solar energy re-radiates from Earth's surface to be absorbed by gasses.

- CO_2 accounts for 18% – 22% of the effect of all such absorbed surface radiation.

- Absorbed energy does not accumulate. It rises 15km – 20km by convection.

- Radiation of energy to space at those altitudes allows descent of cold air by convection.

- Energy emitted by the surface can only be absorbed in definite quanta.

- Such energy can only be absorbed within very limited wavelength frequencies.

But it is saturation of the CO_2 absorbing frequencies that falsifies global warming dogma.

Saturation occurs at the point at which no further electromagnetic infra red surface radiation is capable of being absorbed by CO_2 molecules whose dipole moments (electrons) interact with it.

Saturation and climate activist dogma

At the core of the climate activist dogma is the false doctrine that more CO_2 in the atmosphere means more global warming.

There are so many such assertions that it is taken as an axiom[61]. It is the basic but most serious and false assumption that informs the repeated statements of the IPCC and the catechism of the global warming 'consensus'. We are told that we are at a 'tipping point' which will be irreversible once passed. It would seem inevitable that if CO_2 density intensifies its radiative effect would also intensify in proportion thus creating a runaway warming phenomenon.

However this is in reality a cynical suppression of the known and true position in physics. The very founders of the global warming dogma were not only aware of the truth as to the physics of the phenomenon of saturation but actually promoted the deception as to its effects.

Climate environmentalism as propagated by its founding devotees was intended to overthrow the status quo of western economies. It was launched by a small and extreme socialist group at Stanford University USA centred on Dr Stephen Schneider Professor of Environmental Biology and Global Change in the early 1970s. It gave impetus to the Club of Rome which first enunciated the environmentalist dogma. It was Schneider who declared:-

> *"To capture the public imagination we have to offer up some scary scenarios, make simple dramatic statements and little mention of any doubts one might have. Each of us has to strike the right balance between being effective and being honest[62]"*

The means by which the believers would procure a new order was described in the blueprint for the 21st century in published in 1991[63]. It has a sub-title "A Report by the Council of the Club of Rome".

---

[61] UK Prime Minister B Johnson Opening Speech CoP Climate Conference November 2021. "*…quilting the Earth in an invisible and suffocating blanket of CO_2 raising temperature of the planet with a speed and an abruptness that is entirely man made*". Goddard Institute for Space Sciences For example "*Adding more CO_2 to the atmosphere is like putting another blanket on the bed*". British Geological Survey "*CO_2 released from the burning of fossil fuels is accumulating as an insulating blanket around the Earth trapping more of the Sun's heat in our atmosphere*".

[62] Dr Stephen Schneider "Discover" October 1989.

[63] The First Global Revolution_ A Report by the Council of the Club of Rome – Alexander King, Bertrand Schneider – - Random House, Inc Pantheon Books (1991).

It expounds the essence of activist environmentalism. It asserts that to achieve the sought for global change new enemies had to be found. It notes that, historically, social or political unity has commonly been motivated by enemies in common:

> "The need for enemies seems to be a common historical factor....In searching for a new enemy to unite us, we came up with the idea that pollution, the threat of global warming, water shortages, famine and the like would fit the bill....All these dangers are caused by human intervention and it is only through changed attitudes and behaviour can they be overcome. The real enemy then is humanity itself"

It is indeed shocking to discover that Dr Stephen Schneider himself declared that saturation precluded further global warming even at many multiples of increased CO_2 concentrations.

He correctly claimed that with increased atmospheric content of CO_2 – even by a factor of 10 – the **"runaway greenhouse effect will not occur because the 15 micron CO_2 band, which is the main source of absorption, 'saturates'"**. He declared that the increase in the global temperature caused by CO_2 in the next 30 years "will be as small as 0.1K"[64].

Nor could this be doubted by those with knowledge of the physics of CO_2 absorption of radiation. There had never been any correlation between rise in temperature of the Earth and CO_2 concentrations. Temperature had not increased in line with CO_2 over geological ages or in the previous 2,500 years. During severe glaciations in the Ordovician minimum, Triassic and mid Jurassic periods CO_2 density had been up to eight times the present level.

That is because above very low levels of density CO_2 cannot absorb more than negligible radiation due to saturation as Schneider correctly stated. To explain this we need to understand that CO_2 is not climate sensitive over a certain density.

Climate Sensitivity. Doubling of CO_2

Climate sensitivity is the increase (if any) in global average temperature that is expected to have occurred at a time when the atmospheric CO_2 concentration has doubled.

This depends entirely on the extent to which CO_2 is capable within the limits of physics of absorbing infra red surface radiation. As set out above Max Planck was able to delineate the spectrum of radiation from warm bodies. He established what is known as the Planck curve which appears as the blue curve in Figure 15 below.

The actual infra-red radiation from Earth to space is described by the jagged black line in Figure 15. This was defined by Karl Schwarzchild (1873-1916). Actual radiation intensities in the presence of the thermal resistance deployed by greenhouse gasses in the atmosphere could now be delineated.

It has now been possible to calculate climate sensitivity precisely – namely the degree (if any) to which temperature of the atmosphere will increase with a doubling of CO_2 density. The results of this important research were published[65] in 2021.

---

[64] Rasool, S.I., and S.H. Schneider, 1971: Atmospheric carbon dioxide and aerosols: Effects of large increases on global climate. *Science*, 173, 138-141, doi:10.1126/science.173.3992.138. Cited by Zbigniew Jaworowski Nature Rules the Climate First Published January 1, 2005 Research Article https://doi.org/10.1260/0958305053516163.

[65] Relative Potency of Greenhouse Molecules Professors W. A. van Wijngaarden and W. Happer Cornell University arXiv:2103.16465 [physics.ao-ph] or arXiv:2103.16465v1 ttps://doi.org/10.48550/arXiv.2103.1646. Also see Dependence of Earth's Thermal Radiation on Five Most Abundant Greenhouse Gasses. Professors W. A. van Wijngaarden and W. Happer Cornell University.

Calculation of climate sensitivity

The study constitutes a comprehensive analysis of atmospheric 'forcings' namely the effect of greenhouse gasses upon thermal radiation on a doubling of CO_2 density. It involved downloading spectral lines and transition frequencies of over 1.3 million rovibrational[67] lines from the most recent HITRAN [68] data- bases in order to calculate the per-molecule forcings of the most important greenhouse gas molecules.

Accurate calculations of radiative forcing[69] are essential to any estimate of future climate change. The analysis examined the effect of changing greenhouse gas concentrations on thermal radiation in the case of a clear sky.

The results were plotted within the Planck curve of theoretical maximum radiation. That revealed a plot of actual radiation intensities at a surface temperature of 15°C (288.7K) as impacted by greenhouse gasses. This depiction is described by the jagged black line in Figure 15.

The horizontal scale is the frequency of thermal radiation. The vertical scale is the thermal power going out to space. If there were no greenhouse gasses the radiation into space would be all that is comprised within the blue curve.

The key element of this graph is the red line. This is the furthest limit on what the Earth would radiate into space if the concentration of CO_2 were to double its current atmospheric volume. The green line shows the radiation from Earth to space in the hypothetical absence of all CO_2.

Figure 15

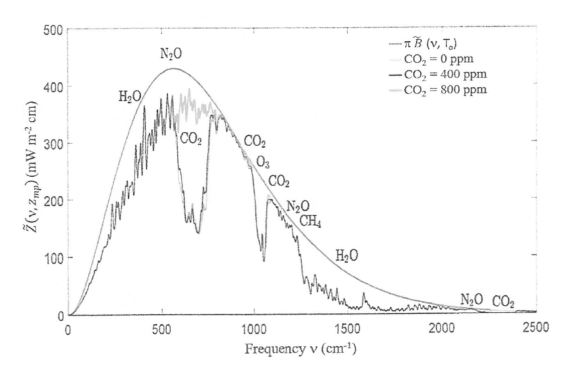

---

[67] Rotational–vibrational spectroscopy is concerned with infrared of molecules in the gas phase. Transitions involving changes in both vibrational and rotational states are ' rovibrational' (or ro-vibrational) transitions. When these emit or absorb photons (electromagnetic radiation), the frequency is proportional to the difference in energy levels and can be detected by certain kinds of spectroscopy.

[68] HITRAN (an acronym for High Resolution Transmission) molecular spectroscopic database used to simulate and analyse the transmission and emission of light in gaseous media, with an emphasis on planetary atmospheres. VAMDC (Virtual Atomic and Molecular Data Centre) atomic and molecular (A&M) data compiled within a set of AM databases.

[69] A climate 'forcing' is any influence on climate that originates from outside the climate system itself. The climate system includes the oceans, land surface, cryosphere, biosphere, and atmosphere. Examples of external forcings include surface reflectivity (albedo); .human induced changes are greenhouse gases and aerosols from industrial output.

The gap (bridged by the green line) is caused by CO_2 absorbing radiation from Earth that would otherwise go into space. If CO_2 density is doubled it does not double the gap. All that happens is that a minuscule difference is established between the black curve (base density) and the red curve (double density). The minute additional absorption of energy occurs at the weak extremities of the 14-16 micron frequency bands. ·

The calculations and research show that with a doubling of atmospheric CO_2 from a surface at a temperature of 15^0C (288.7K) the consequent increase in temperature increase is just 3.0 watts per square metre or 1^0C. Such an increase is so negligible as to be of no consequence whatsoever. The passing of a cloud over the sun would be more noticeable.

Correspondence with satellite evidence

These calculations have been confirmed, to an extraordinary degree of correspondence, by empirical observations. Figure 16 shows intensities of radiation emitted as measured by an interferometer in a satellite. Radiation was measured for the Sahara desert, Mediterranean and for Antarctica. The radiation attenuation – and therefore warming – due to greenhouse gasses is shown in relation to the Planck curve (red dotted line) of gas free radiation intensity. It should be noted that the Antarctica graph shows an increase not a decrease in radiation. That is because the temperature of the air a few kilometres above the surface increases so prompting release of radiation.

Figure 16 shows excellent correspondence of calculations with empirical observations.

Figure 16

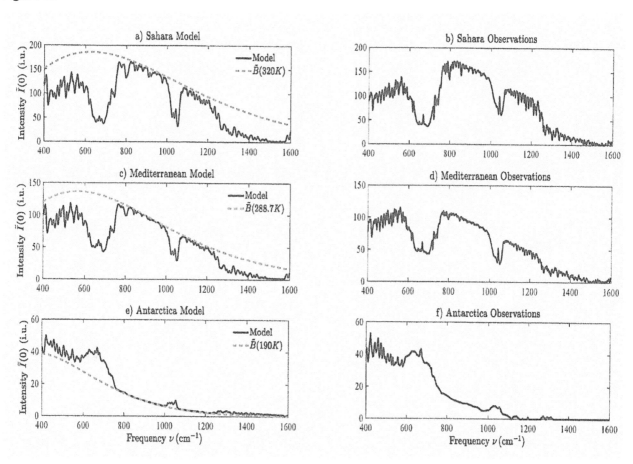

The effect of increasing the density of CO_2 is to raise the height in the atmosphere at which radiation is emitted. It simply means it is cooled by higher levels of cold temperature.

The paramount cause for this severe limitation on the potency of CO_2 molecules to have any noticeable impact on the Earth's temperature is the phenomenon of saturation.

Logarithmic decline of CO_2 absorption of radiation

The absorption capacity of CO_2 is effectively logarithmic.

The first 20ppm has the most potent effect on temperature. After 280 ppm CO_2 has absorbed virtually all the infra-red radiation that it can absorb as shown in Figure 17. The graph illustrates the exponential decline of the warming effect of the gas.

Saturation due to absorption is a common phenomenon and may be seen analogously in the case of blotting paper. With relatively small and finite volumes of ink adding more blotting paper does not absorb more ink.

An analogy would be the use of sunglasses. The first pair blocks say 60% of sunlight. Two pairs reduce it to 24%. The next pair it is 9.6% and then 3.8%, the next it is 1.54% and so on.

Figure 17

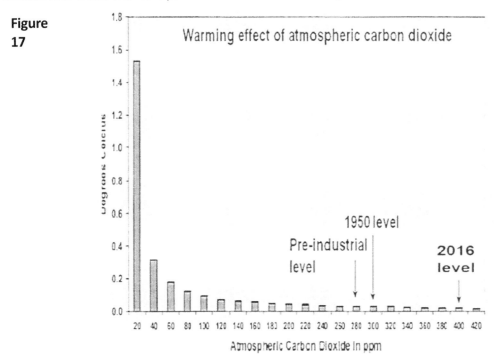

Doubling the concentrations of CO_2 to 834ppm accounts for only a further 1^0C increase in temperature. A further doubling to 1,668ppm would have scarcely any appreciable effect due to the exponential effect of saturation. As has been noted, that was no more than the emphatic conclusion of Dr Stephen Schneider the founder of environmental climate dogma himself.

No amplifying factors

By the time of its later 'reports' the IPCC recognised that saturation of the CO_2 absorption bands with surface radiation dismantles the entire structure of 'global warming' theory. It therefore put up 'positive feedback' as an attempt to defend it. The IPCC attempts to argue that heat due to the greenhouse effect of CO_2 warms the atmosphere to such and extent as to cause increased water vapour concentration due to evaporation. The water vapour then acts as a greenhouse gas and thus amplifies molecular heating from surface radiation.

The entire IPCC hypothesis of CO_2 generated global warming depends upon this contention.

It asserts a form of colossal positive feedback from the 20% of greenhouse effect attributable to CO_2 which it conjectures causes an amplification of warming by a factor of no less than 4.5 times.

There are four fundamental flaws in this hypothesis.

Negative feedback principle

The term 'feedback' refers to the effect that occurs when the output of a system becomes an input to the same system. Feedback loops may be positive or negative. Positive feedback occurs when the effects of an original change are amplified or accelerated to produce an exponential increase in the effect. In contrast negative feedback occurs when the effects of an initial change are counteracted to restore the equilibrium.

It is rare in natural conditions for positive feedback to occur though they are found in explosives. Le Chatelier's principle[70] states that if a dynamic equilibrium is disturbed by changing the conditions then the position of the equilibrium shifts to counteract the change and to re-establish and equilibrium. This is a fundamental principle of science.

For example, as the temperature of the Earth rises the Stefan Bolzmann law states that the emission of infrared radiation back into space from the surface will increase exponentially. By increasing the amount of outgoing radiation as the Earth warms there is a slight cooling effect. This type of negative feedback is also known as the Planck feedback[71].

No runaway effect over geological past

Positive feedback as postulated by the IPCC essentially would create a runaway amplification of the condition of the disturbed equilibrium. This predicates an exponential repeating increase in the greenhouse effect of intensified water vapour operating as the dominant of all greenhouse gasses as well as the retention of more heat in the atmosphere.

It will readily be seen that such a runaway effect even would not simply be confined to the modern era alone but would apply in all geological eras in which atmospheric CO_2 was at least as dense as today and particularly when density much greater. However, as set out above, during the severe glaciation in the Ordovician minimum CO2 density was ten times today's level. In the Permian, Triassic and early/mid Jurassic periods temperature was at its highest for the past 600m years whilst CO_2 density fell from 3500ppm to 400ppm rising over 100m years only to 1500ppm by the beginning of the Jurassic period as can be seen in Figures 1 and 3.

Moreover temperature was maintained at over 25° C for 60 million years from the end of the Cretaceous period while CO_2 density fell from 1,800ppm to 700ppm. The 1938 to 1976 rise in CO_2 density from 300 to 335ppm were years of severe cold with the worst winters of the 20th century in 1947 and 1963.

---

[70] His 1884 formulation was "Every system in stable chemical equilibrium submitted to the influence of and exterior force which tends to cause variation either in its temperature or its condensation (pressure, concentration, number of molecules in the unit of volume) in its totality or only in some one of its parts can undergo only those interior modification which, if they occur alone, would produce a change of temperature, or of condensation, of a sign contrary to that resulting from the exterior force.

[71] Zong-Liang Yang. (October 10, 2015). Chapter 2: *The Global Energy Balance* [Online].

Inadequacy of CO₂ greenhouse warming

No human induced warming could cause water vapour concentrations at the level adequate to account for increase in temperature over the past 70 years when CO_2 emissions began their significant upward trend. Even at the levels of CO_2 density in 1850 there has been saturation of radiation in the available frequency bands save to a negligible extent. The IPCC do not dispute the existence of the phenomenon of saturation. It has been shown the doubling existing densities would increase heat by just 3 Wm^2. Such a minimal increase would be barely noticeable and entirely ineffective to induce surface water evaporation or increase in humidity.

Humidity and clouds

Humidity is a measurement of the amount of water vapour in the air. Warmer air holds more water vapour than cooler air if water is freely available. The vapour component makes up about 99% of all water held in the atmosphere.

Relative Humidity measures how close the air is to being saturated – the proportion in which actual water vapour content bears to potential content at the same temperature. Warmer air holds more water vapour since more is available. If the RH of the air is 100% it is said to be fully saturated.

Figure 18

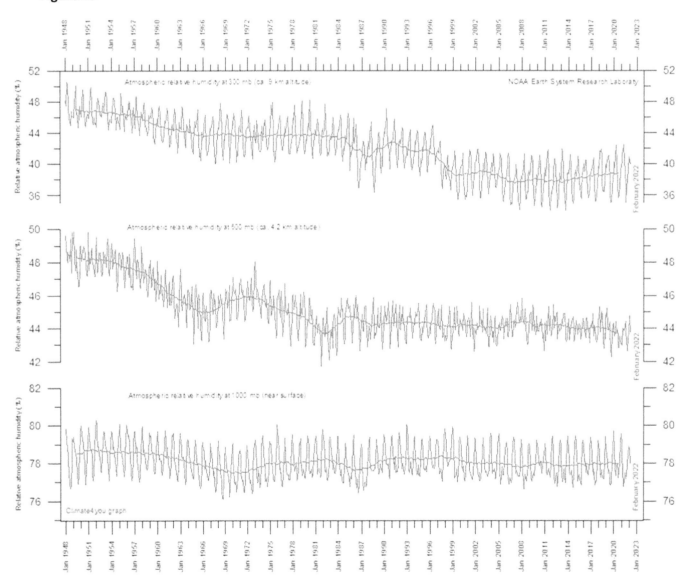

Figure18 shows that this has not been the case since 1948.

It depicts relative atmospheric humidity (%) at three different altitudes in the lower part of the atmosphere (the troposphere) since January 1948. The thin blue lines show monthly values, while the thick blue lines show the running 37 month average.[72]

If the IPCC theory of positive feedback had been well founded a significant increase in water vapour content to match the 38% rise in CO_2 density over the 74 year period would have been observed.

However close to the Earth's surface the relative humidity has remained roughly constant though with variations. In the remaining layers of the atmosphere there has been a definite decline.

SUMMARY

At densities over pre-industrial levels (280ppm) atmospheric CO_2 has negligible capacity to absorb infra red energy radiation from the Earth's surface. Doubling today's CO_2 level of 417ppm will increase average surface heat by no more than 3.0 watts per square metre or just 1^0C. Such increase would be so small as to be of no consequence at all. Doubling again to 1600ppm would have no greater effect.

---

[72] Climate 4U Professor Ole Humlum. Data source: Earth System Research Laboratory (NOAA). Diagram update: 11 March 2022.

PART 3

Look deep into nature, and then you will understand everything better.

Albert Einstein.

IX.   CO$_2$ & PAST TEMPERATURE

It has been shown that CO$_2$ has a minor though important role in maintaining Earth's surface temperature at an average of 15^{0}C. It does so by absorbing 18% – 22% of the 6% of the sun's radiation which is emitted from the surface – or 1.08% – 1.32%. It has no other warming effect.

The IPCC dogma declares that temperature of the Earth has risen and will continue to rise to such an extent and at such a rate as to put humanity's existence at risk.

These two statements cannot both be true. Accordingly it is essential to consider the evidence for each of them.

If the evidence of the geological past and of present times is that CO$_2$, at any density, has not caused rise in temperature of the Earth other than to help to maintain it at a level that is agreeable for life and welfare then that concludes matters.

In science belief cannot displace evidence. Evidence is afforded by empirical observation. Evidence can only be provided by the past and the present. Predictions of future temperature that are not supported by evidence are of no more value than conjecture or belief.

Two questions have to be addressed.

- Does the evidence show that CO$_2$ has caused global warming in the past?

- Does the evidence show that it Is doing so now?

Any theory of causation which does not give rise to correlation[73] with the effect cannot be valid.

Is there any compelling correlation of the rise in temperature with the rise of CO$_2$ atmospheric density over geological past?

The past 550m years represents the time since the emergence of multicellular life. For the past 423,000 years there exists evidence from Antarctic ice cores affording clear data on the extent of temperature variations and their relation to CO$_2$ concentrations in the atmosphere.

550,000,000 year record.

It has been seen that the temperature and CO$_2$ density of the atmosphere have diverged widely over the geological ages since the appearance of multicellular animal life and of plants and trees.

The diagram of variations in temperature and CO$_2$ density of the atmosphere set out below has been set out in Figure 1 but it serves also to demonstrate the lack of correlation of CO$_2$ and temperature variations.

CO$_2$ density varies in temperate periods with photosynthetic consumption and in glacial periods with absorption by oceans and photorespiration of plants as is explained in Part 4.

Temperature is governed by solar cycles, great ocean shifts, the Milankovitch orbital cycles and extreme volcanic activity as well as other lesser factors.

---

[73] a mutual or reciprocal relationship between two or more phenomena.

Figure 19

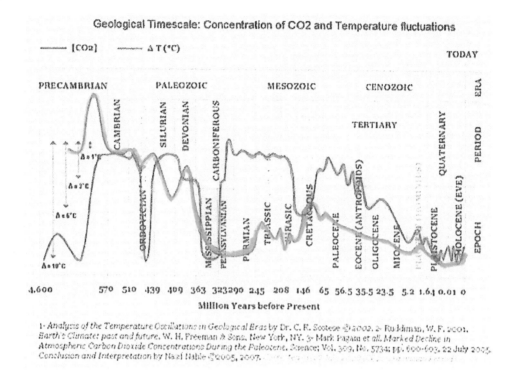

Geological Timescale: Concentration of CO2 and Temperature fluctuations

Figure 19 discloses no causal correlation of rise in temperature with rise of CO_2 atmospheric density. Indeed for hundreds of millions of years there is an adverse contrary trend. In particular from the Late Carboniferous period to the early Cretaceous period – a span of 190 million years – CO_2 was at its lowest average density and average temperature was at its highest.

423,000 years before present

Geology is concerned with the physical structure, substance and processes of the Earth.

For the past four ice ages, over 423,000 years, warming preceded increased density of atmospheric CO_2. The Vostok Antarctica Research Station ice cores provide samples of a fundamental feature of the deglaciation cycles or 'interglacials' as they are often described. These ice cores of up to 3,310 metres confirm the glaciation cycles at between 87,000 to 123,000 years. Antarctic temperatures varied by 10^0C and atmospheric density varied between 180 ppm and 300 ppm. A further source is the European Project for Ice Coring in Antarctica (EPICA) Dome C.

Figure 20

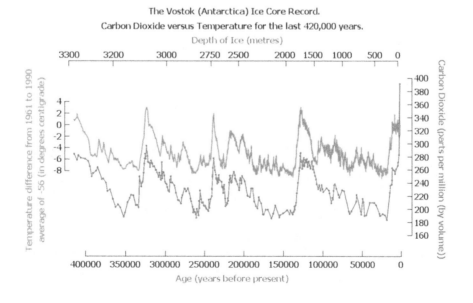

The Vostok (Antarctica) Ice Core Record.
Carbon Dioxide versus Temperature for the last 420,000 years.

Figure 20 above depicts temperatures and changes in CO_2 concentrations shown by the Vostok ice cores. The glaciations and interglaciations are caused by the Earth's orbital eccentricity cycles around the Sun (Milankovitch cycle). Data is plotted in chronological order.

Temperature changes induce changes in atmospheric CO_2 and CH_4 (methane). The seas form 71% of the surface of the Earth. The oceans hold 39,000bn tonnes of carbon being 19 times as much carbon as the terrestrial biosphere which comprises all plants and the underlying soils on our planet. The solubility of CO_2 in water varies greatly with changes in atmospheric temperature. It is at its highest in cold temperatures. Rise in temperature of the oceans reduces solubility of CO_2 resulting in emissions to the atmosphere.

Figure 20 reveals a striking proportionality between temperature increase and rise in CO_2 concentrations. At the opening of each cycle the range of rise and fall of temperature is over periods of approximately 7,000 to 16,000 years. For CO_2 the range is from 14,000 to 23,000 years. There is a lagging period between rise of temperature and CO_2 of about 7,000 years. A shorter period of lagging occurs for the less severe peaks with periods of 800 to 1,000 years about the average.

It will be seen that with falling temperature CO_2 concentrations do not immediately fall. They decline relatively gradually as the solubility of the oceans increases.

The most abundant source of readily available CO_2 in the carbon cycle is the oceans. It accounts for the increases in CO_2 density revealed by the ice core data. It is released with warming of the atmosphere. The long term global average of sea surface temperature is 15°C. At this level seawater can dissolve its own volume of CO_2. At 10°C it absorbs 19% more but at 20°C it absorbs 12% less.

Similar lagging is shown over the past 20,000 years by the EPICA ice core data.

Figure 21

The EPICA Dome C ice cores, 560 km south of Vostok, are further confirmation that rises in temperature precede and do not cause rise in CO_2 density. For all of the graph's 20,000 years CO_2 has not driven global warming. The inverse is the case.

Timescales of 150 years are laughably inadequate to base any reliable conclusions as to the phenomena that govern climate variations. It is only by reference to the causes of de-glaciation and glaciation, orbital cycles, solar radiation, and atmospheric conditions that any useful scientific conclusions can be proposed.

Last 2,500 years

Temperature fluctuations have been a characteristic of climate during the entire Holocene epoch in which we find ourselves. The Greenland oxygen isotope records provide a reliable record. Figure 22[74] reveals that there were at least 22 major temperature fluctuations over 10,000 years prior to 1960 when CO_2 levels started to rise steeply. None of these could have been caused by increased CO_2 as all preceded the rise of CO_2 density levels.

Figure 22

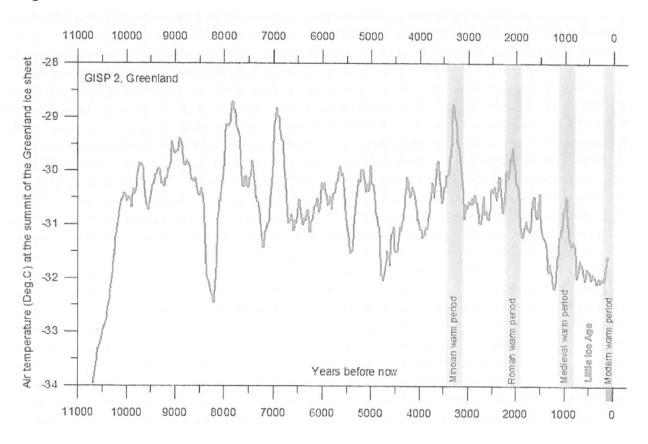

Central Greenland temperature changes, though not precisely identical to global temperature changes, do reflect global temperature changes with a decadal-scale delay[75] except for the Antarctic region which is in opposite phase.[76]

The principal global temperature variations for the past 2,500 years have been the Roman Warming Period, the Medieval Warming Period and the Little Ice Age. During each of these periods, together extending over 2,500 years, CO_2 atmospheric concentrations have remained within a range of 260 – 280 ppm. These periods saw pronounced variations of temperature.

These major shifts of temperatures require examination as the IPCC has sought to eliminate them from their graphs. This has been done to enable it to fabricate graphs showing a causal and linear correlation of temperature rise and CO_2 intensification. It was done in the 'hockey stick' scandal of the 2001 'report'. It has now been done in the 2021 'report'[77].

---

[74] See Professor Ole Humlum Climate4U *Global Temperatures*.

[75] Box, J.E., Yang, L., Bromwich, D.H. and Bau, L.-S. 2009. *Greenland Ice Sheet Surface Air Temperature Variability*: 1840–2007. Journal of Climate 22, 4029-4049.

[76] Chylek, P., Folland, C.K., Lesins, G. and Manvendra, K.D. 2010. *Twentieth century bipolar seesaw of the Arctic and Antarctic surface air temperatures.* Geophysical Research Letters, 37, L08703, doi: 10.1029/2010GL042793.

[77] See graph (a) set out in the Summary for Policymakers August 2021 presented at CoP26 Glasgow.

Roman Warming Period

A recent study of data from the Sicily Channel[78] has confirmed the existence of very warm conditions of the period from 250 BC to 400 AD. It was based on measurements of calcium carbonate deposits of surface plankton marine creatures[79] close to the oxygen isotopic equilibrium which is temperature sensitive and so makes it a reliable means of establishing past changes.

The record of data of Figure 23 is set out in comparison with previous surface sea temperature reconstructions from the Mediterranean. The study was framed in the context of previously published records from other seas. This comparison is shown together with a complemented record of north hemisphere temperature variations of Figure 24.

These studies confirm the persistent regional occurrence of a distinct warm phase during the Roman Period. The records consistently show the Roman Warming and also the Medieval Warming {see below) as the warmest periods of the last 2,000 years – at least 2°C warmer than current average values.

Figure 23   **Figure 24**

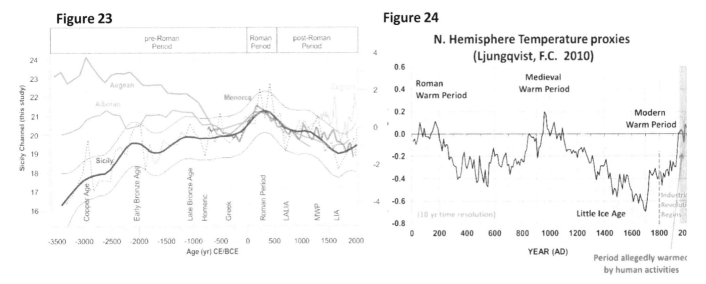

Medieval Warming Period

Regional proxies[80] from around the world establish the existence of a universally much warmer period than today from 900 AD to 1350 AD. This is the Medieval Warm Period or Medieval Climate Optimum. It was a global phenomenon.

The North Hemisphere graph Figure 24 above shows this period most clearly and depicts how temperatures far exceeded those of today. Studies reveal its existence in all parts of the African continent[81]. There is strong evidence also from studies of the sea bed in the Sargasso Sea by the Woods Hole Oceanographic Institute. That sea bed has calcium carbonate deposits of a surface dwelling plankton, as described above, which are dependable means of determining past changes in the temperature of Sargasso Sea surface waters.

---

[78] Margaritelli, G., Cacho, I., Catala, A. *et al.* Persistent warm Mediterranean surface waters during the Roman period. *Sci Rep* 10, 10431 {2020}. https://doi.org/10.1038/s41598-020-67281-2.

[79] Surface dwelling plankton *Globigerinoides ruber*.

[80] Proxy data comprise sources of temperature indications other than direct measurements. They are physical characteristics of the environment preserved to varying degrees. Proxies are natural indicators of climate variability and include data from sources such as tree rings, ice cores, fossil pollen, plankton, ocean sediments, and corals. These allow reconstructions to be made of estimated temperature levels.

[81]Warming and Cooling: *The Medieval Climate Anomaly in Africa and Arabia* Sebastian LOning, Mariusz Gałka,Fritz Vahrenholt First published: 26 October 2017 https://doi.org/10.1002/2017PA003237.

Furthermore temperature variations in the Arctic also show significant rise in temperature from 900 to 1300 AD coinciding with the establishment of farms in Greenland by the Viking population[82].

Figure 25

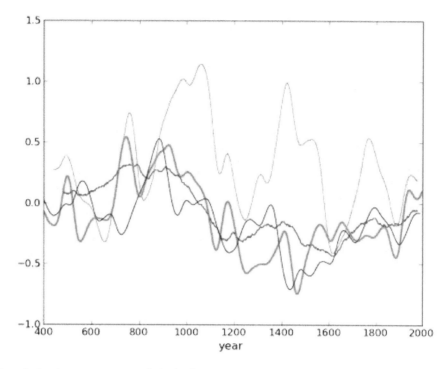

That the Medieval Optimum was a global phenomenon also appears from the following graph[83] of Northern Hemisphere temperature data. As with the Greenland graph it also depicts the severe fall in global temperature over the following 500 years during the Little Ice Age.

Figure 26

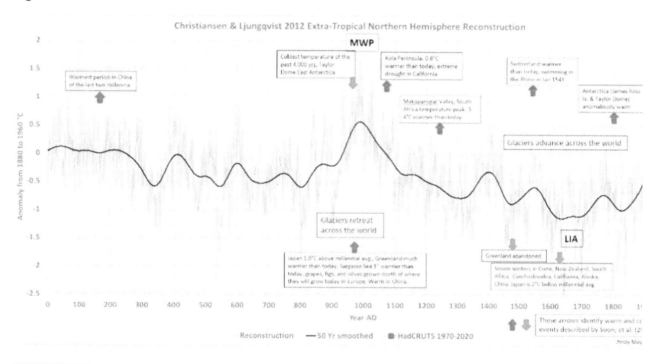

---

[82] At their peak settlements are estimated to have had total population of between 2,000-10,000 inhabitants (sources differ), with archaeologists identifying the ruins of approximately 620 farmsteads around south-western fjords.

[83] Christiansen, B. and Ljungqvist, F. C.: The tropical Northern Hemisphere temperature in the last two millennia: reconstructions of low-frequency variability, Past, 8, 765–786, https://doi.org/10.5194/cp-8-765-2012, 2012.

Last 150 years

Figure 27 depicts the rise of temperature of the Earth following the end of the Little Ice Age[84] as well as the previous warming. From 1800 temperature had begun to rise at a steep rate.

Figure 27

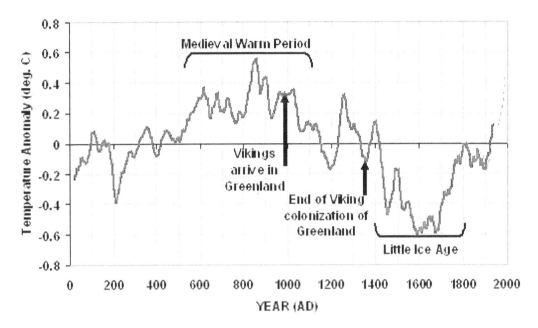

However CO_2 concentrations in the atmosphere only began to increase after 1890. There was a rise to the present day from 280ppm to 417ppm. A gradual rise until 1960 was followed by steep acceleration in a linear curve. But temperature was erratic.

This can be seen from Figure 28. The left hand graph shows CO_2 density rising since 1890. It is that published by NOAA[85]. The right hand graph was that published in 1981 by the promoter of global warming theory James Hansen[86] in the year that he became director of GISS.[87]. This was at a time when severe global cooling had been predicted for over three decades.

Figure 28

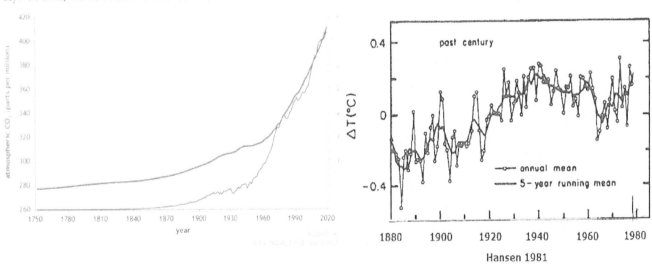

---

[84] See Dr Roy Spencer's website Alabama University. It shows the average of temperature proxies from 12 locations around the Northern Hemisphere as published by Craig Loehle in 2007 and revised in 2008.

[85] US National Ocean and Atmosphere Administration.

[86] James Hansen is the progenitor of the global warming dogma and gave evidence in 1988 to Congress propounding it.

[87] Goddard Institute of Space Studies. One of the official custodians of surface temperature measurement.

The 20th century experienced severe changes of temperature. 1934 was the hottest year of the century in the USA. In the UK the winters of 1947 and 1963 were the coldest since 1740.

Not only did the rise in temperature precede any rise in CO_2 concentrations by 100 years it is also evident that there is no causal correlation between these phenomena. CO_2 density rose by 23% from 1980. Yet as is shown in Figure 38 since 1980 there has been a rise in temperature of only 0.27°C. There has been no warming trend for the last 24 years since 1998 – just a slight fall of 0.22°C.

CO_2 lags behind temperature increase over even very short time spans as shown in Figure 29.

Figure 29[88]

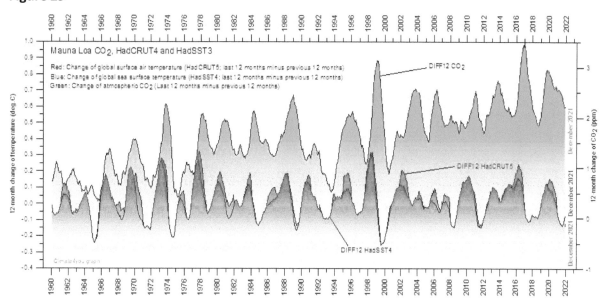

Correlation with Solar output

Whilst there is no correlation of rise of temperature and CO_2 there is a persistent coincidence with solar activity[89]. The following diagrams are evidence of close correlation of solar cycles with temperature over the past 2000 years and over the past 150 years. Figure 30 depicts the Little Ice Age and recovery to modern warming. Figure 31 shows the rise and fall of temperature 1900 – 1976.

Figure 30[90]

Figure 31[91]

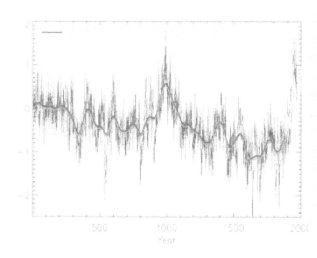

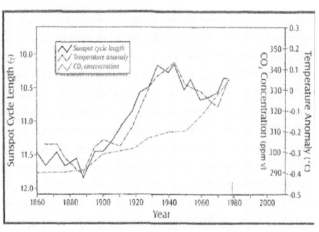

[88] Humlum. O et al. University of Oslo.
[89] Solar natural phenomena occurring within the magnetically heated outer atmospheres in the Sun, including solar wind, radio wave flux, energy bursts such as solar flares, coronal mass ejection or solar eruptions, coronal heating and sunspots. [90] Lungdquist C .http://www.clim-past.net/8/765/2012/cp-8-765-2012.pdf   Northern Hemisphere data.
[91] Plimer Op cit p 131.

Cycles of solar radiance are of various durations. Ice sheet cores and numerous other proxies reveal that they are of 11, 22, 87, 21 and 1500 years. The IPCC climate models do not take account of the critical importance of solar cyclical radiation and none predicted the early 21st century cooling.

The eccentricity of the Earth's orbit round the Sun governs the cycles of glaciation (ice ages) of approximately 90/120,000 years and the interglacial periods of approximately 10/14,000 years.

On a shorter scale the variations in radiative intensity of the Sun correlate with Earth's temperature changes to a significant degree. This is the primary factor that accounts for the temperature rises of the Roman Warming Period, the Medieval Warming Period and the modern warming. It also accounts for sharp decline in temperature during the Little Ice Age.

In Figure 30 above there is correlation with the Roman Warming Period which opens the record. The next notably warm period is the Medieval Optimum 900 – 1300 AD. That is succeeded by the Little Ice Age lasting 500 years when there was no material solar activity. There follows the temperature rise from 1800 to the end of the last century. Currently the Earth is enjoying a warm period with a modest rise in temperature of 1.1^{0}C since 1850 but with no increase over 1998 levels.

Figure 31 shows the 20th century solar activity to 1979 when satellite data replaced surface measurements. It was used by the IPCC in an early report. The 1930s spike and the 1945 – 1976 fall are each shown with precision where the temperature and solar activity closely correlate. There is no correlation at all with rise of CO_2 (lower curve).

Dr Soon[92] has demonstrated in Figure 32 how the Arctic temperatures (Polyakov) correlate extremely well with the total solar irradiance. He also shows (Figure 33) that there is no correlation with CO_2 densities.

Figure 32   **Figure 33**

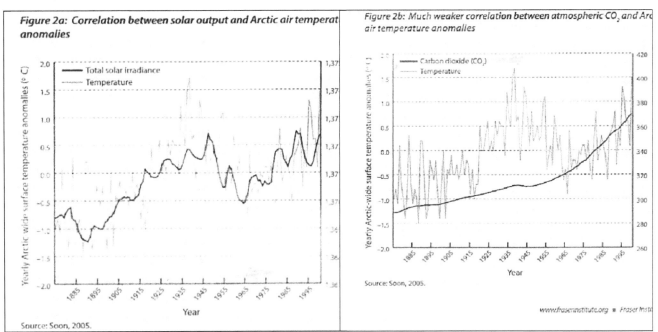

All of these close correlations with solar cycles are so striking as to be compelling.

---

[92] Dr W Soon astrophysicist at the Solar, Stellar and Planetary Sciences Division of the Harvard-Smithsonian Centre for Astrophysics. Founder of Centre for Environmental Research and Earth Sciences (CERES-science.com).

Solar activity has declined over the past two solar cycles[93] as is evident from Figure 34.1. The last cycle (Cycle 24) from 2008 to 2014 was the weakest for 100 years. It accounts for the static trend of temperature for that period.

Figure 34.2 includes a forecast by NOAA of likely solar activity to 2030.

If the current cycle's lower level of intensity is indeed a trend then we can expect noticeable cooling in the future.

Figure 34.1

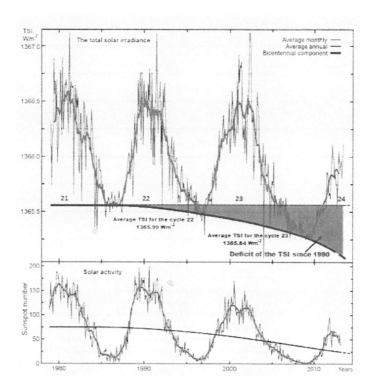

Figure 34.2

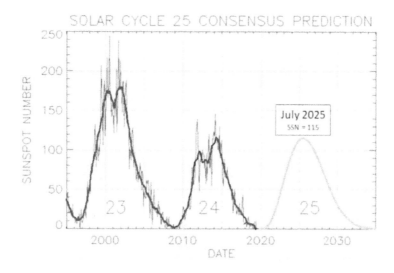

SUMMARY

There must be a necessary correlation between the cause of a phenomenon and its effect. There is close correlation of temperature with solar activity. The absence of any causal correlation of rise in temperature and CO_2 density at any time in the geological and recent past invalidates the hypothesis that CO_2 is a driver of 'global warming'.

[93] Professor Easterbrook *Evidence Based Climate Science* Elsevier Inc 2016 p 311.

III.   CO₂ & RECENT TEMPERATURE

Measurement of the Earth's temperature provides the evidence on which judgment may be made as to warming or cooling. So much is axiomatic.

Satellite and balloon radiosonde observed measurements provide a gold standard of global temperature data. Surface temperature records from weather stations are unreliable and are prone to manipulation.

Sources of data

For the years to 1979 surface thermometer readings are the primary source of temperature information. They are maintained by two entities - the Climate Research Unit working with the Met Office's Hadley Centre in Essex and the Goddard Institute of Space Sciences[94] in New York.

Satellite and balloon sonde measurements are maintained by the University of Alabama at Huntsville under Professor John Christy and Dr Roy Spencer. Another satellite record is kept by Remote Sensing Systems though it is less comprehensive.

Since 1979 measurement of atmospheric temperature has been made much more precise and reliable by introduction of satellite and balloon sondes. These cover the entire planet. They provide daily readings of different levels of the atmosphere. They are not concentrated in industrialised Western countries as are surface measurements. They cover the oceans equally as well as the land.

Defects of surface records[95].

Surface temperature measurements derived from thermometers have serious limitations. They are greatly affected by local conditions including urban siting and the heat island effect[96], back reflections from structures, height above ground, changes in the size and materials of the required 'Stevenson Screen' – the box which houses thermometers. Approximately 50% of the US weather stations do not fulfil the requirements of the US government and introduce a warming bias.

Loss of weather stations has impaired efficacy. In the mid 1970s there were 6,000 weather stations: there are now less than 1,500 with a disproportionate loss to rural areas. Most of those closed were cool, high altitude, high latitude, rural, and remote locations. The remaining stations are concentrated in populated industrialised Western countries and a much higher proportion are now in or are directly affected by built up areas or airports. Over 80% of the surface of the planet and 90% of the oceans have no coverage of instrumental temperature readings including vast areas of Russia, Africa, Canada, and Antarctica.

For these reasons the shortcomings of previous temperature measurements should only be relied on for temperature records prior to 1979. For the past 43 years sophisticated observation and measurement by satellite and balloon sondes must prevail in case of any conflict or inconsistency with surface measurements.

---

[94] The Goddard Institute for Space Sciences was until 2013 run by Dr James Hansen an impassioned believer in the dogma of global warming. With the present director G A Schmid, he has been responsible for the GISS distortions of data. His evidence to the US Senate Committee on Energy and Natural Resource in 1988 was that the 4 hottest years in 100 years recorded since the advent of recorded measurements had been in the 1980s rising to a peak in 1987. This was false. It put 'global warming' into the public arena. His statements are at the extreme end of environmentalist predictions of catastrophe including his warning to President Obama that *"he had only 4 years to save the world"*. He called for CEO's of major fossil fuel companies to be put on trial for *"high crimes against humanity and nature"* for spreading disinformation about global warming. He described coal fired power plants as the *"factories of death"* and the *"trains carrying coal to power stations are death trains"*. *"Climate change is analogous to Lincoln and Slavery – Churchill and Nazism.".*

[95] Plimer Op cit p 377 and authorities cited. See also Professor D Easterbrook Op Cit Chapter 2

[96] Reflection from roads, pavements, domestic heating, factories, vehicles, machinery, shopping centres, power lines. T R Oke 1988. The Urban Energy Balance Progress in Physical Geography 12 471-508.

By far the greatest concentration of surface temperature measuring stations is to be found in the US. By 1997 US surface temperature data had failed to show a steady warming trend and was showing a cooling trend from the 1940s. It also showed the universally accepted fact in the climate science community that the 1930s was by far the hottest period in recent times.

The average annual surface temperature data from the USHCNS[97] issued by NOAA for the period to 1995 show an average cooling trend since the late-1930s with an uplift from 1977.

Figure 36

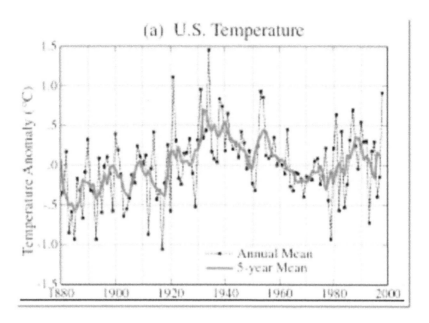

Similar trends are revealed by Arctic ice core data.

Figure 37

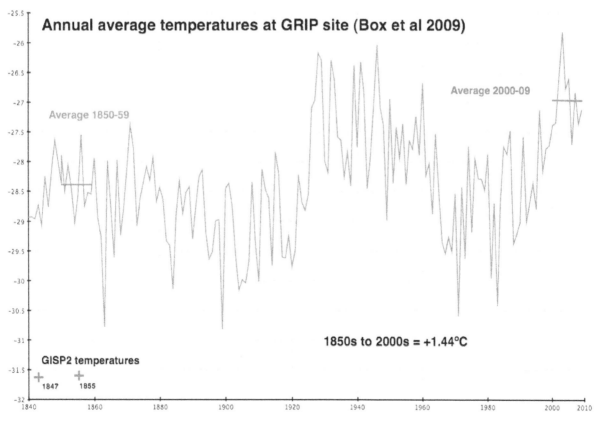

---

[97] United States Historical Climatology Network Stations.

As explained above Central Greenland temperature changes, though not precisely identical to global temperature changes, do reflect global temperature changes[98] .

Satellite and Balloon radiosonde measurements

The University of Alabama in Huntsville USA (UAH) has since 1979 published global temperature data each month derived daily from orbiting satellites and balloon radio sonde data. The record is the most comprehensive body of observations derived from emissions from oxygen in the atmosphere. The intensity of these signals is in direct proportion to temperature.

The satellite instruments measure the temperature of the atmosphere from the surface up to an altitude of about 8 kilometres above sea level. Very accurate records are obtained by measuring variation of microwaves from oxygen molecules. Balloon sondes report temperature at many levels. These sources provide reliable and consistent observed trends of atmospheric temperature. In addition planet-wide weather centres generate data on atmospheric conditions from satellites, balloons and other observations to create a continuously running model known as Reanalyses.

The UAH data show warming of the atmosphere since January 1980 of only $0.27^{\circ}C$. This is in the very lowest sets of warming estimates put up by the IPCC which assume scarcely any CO_2 increase. But in reality CO_2 density in the atmosphere has increased since 1978 by 77 ppm – that is by 23%. Moreover, for CO_2 to be a driver of surface warming the air where the greenhouse effect occurs must warm at a greater rate than the surface. But the opposite is the case.

Thus the most accurate and appropriate physical evidence does not at all support the dogma the CO_2 causes dangerous warming. Figure 38 shows temperature changes for last 43 years.

Figure 38

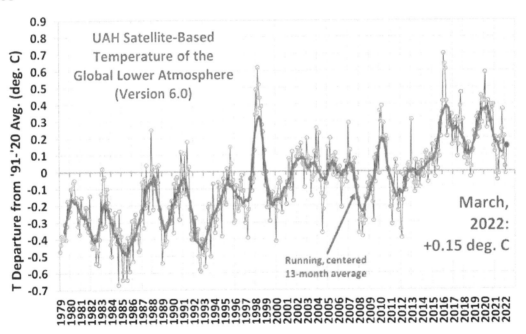

The satellite/balloon record correlates with known naturally occurring phenomena. The dominant factors in the record are the El Nino[99] spikes over these years. These included the El Nino spikes of 1982/3, 1987/8, 1991, 1997/8, 2015/6 as well as the La Nina spikes of 2010/2011 and 2020/2021.

Average global temperature has fallen by $0.22^{\circ}C$ since 1998.

---

[98] Chylek, P., Folland, C.K., Lesins, G. and Manvendra, K.D. 2010. *Twentieth century bipolar seesaw of the Arctic and Antarctic surface air temperatures.* Geophysical Research Letters, 37, L08703, doi: 10.1029/2010GL042793.
[99] Irregularly occurring series of climatic changes affecting the equatorial Pacific, characterized by the appearance of unusually warm, nutrient-poor water off northern Peru and Ecuador, typically in late December. The effects of El Niño include reversal of wind patterns across the Pacific, drought in Australasia, and unseasonal heavy rain in South America.

How does this gold standard observational record of global temperature relate to the climate models used by the IPCC which are all based on assumptions as to the imputed effect of CO_2? To explain and illustrate this AUH[100] was able to set the actual trend of climate variation against simulated changes based on climate models[101].

Figure 39 shows the average of 102 climate models of the IPCC derived from the CMIP5 models [102] used by the IPCC shown against the actual observed atmospheric temperature record from three sources of data – satellite, balloon, and reanalyses.

Figure 40 shows the Extended Reconstructed Sea Surface Temperature {ERSST} dataset[103] of ocean surface temperature and the latest CMIP6 climate model simulations which underwrite the IPCC 2021 'report'. The plot shows the monthly global (60N-60S) average ocean surface temperature variations from 1979 to 2016 for 68 model simulations from 13 different climate models. The 43 years of observations 1979 {bold black line} shows warming as occurring much more slowly than the average climate model says it should have. The rate of warming is 50% of what is being modelled. As seen from Figure 38 temperature has fallen since 2016 so widening the disparity.

Figure 39

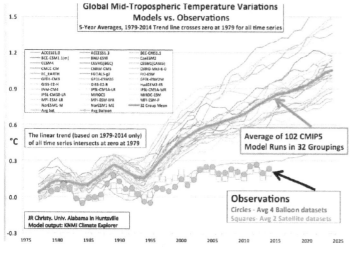

Figure 40

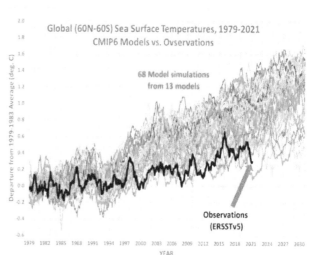

- The models show a vast divergence from actual observational measurements. Evidence given at a hearing before the US House Science Committee[104] is that the IPCC modelled trend is *"Highly significantly different from the observations"*.

- There is an absurd variation in the ranges of modelled temperatures themselves. In Figure 39 there is so great a variation as to render averaging meaningless. In Figure 40 consider the blue line at the top right hand corner predicted for the next decade and its remoteness from the yellow line at the bottom right hand corner.

---

[100] Alabama University of Huntsville. Official record of global satellite and balloon radiosonde temperature data.

[101] Testimony of John R. Christy Professor Atmospheric Science University of Alabama to US House Committee on Science, Space and Technology 12th March 2017.

[102] Coupled Model Intercomparison Project Phase 5 The basis of IPCC modelling.

[103] A global monthly sea surface temperature dataset derived from the International Comprehensive Ocean–Atmosphere Dataset {ICOADS}. Diagram Dr Roy Spencer University of Alabama *An Earth Day Reminder: "Global Warming" is Only ~so% of What Models Predict"*. The graph has been updated since data is still being released but the graph is not materially affected. [104] Testimony of John R Christy Professor of Atmospheric Science University of Alabama to U.S House Committee on Science Space and Technology 29th March 2017.

Conclusion

The IPCC model trends grossly exaggerate the actual observational trend.

But when the models were run **excluding** the factor of added CO_2 they performed far better against the observations.

This is due to the fact that increased CO_2 density in the atmosphere has negligible effect on temperature[105] (see Section VIII). The IPCC models algorithms are programmed with a strong CO_2 bias factor and it is this that creates the distortion.

The models are false and of no value except to reveal their invalidity.

A temperature increase of approximately 1.1^0C since pre-industrial time is substantially accountable for by the fact that the planet has been emerging from the Little Ice Age, the rise being attributable almost certainly to increase in solar activity (see Section IX Figures 34.1 and 34.2).

SUMMARY

CO_2 has no influence on global temperature beyond slowing down by convection the escape of solar energy rising from the Earth's before being radiated to space and so causing cold air to cool the atmosphere. Increase in global temperature since 1800 has been due to heightened solar activity following emergence from the Little Ice Age. Over the 42 years since 1980 temperature has risen by only 0.27^0C. Global temperature has fallen since 1998 by 0.22^0C.

---

[105] Testimony of John R Christy as above. See also *Relative Potency of Greenhouse Molecules*. Professor W A Wijngaarden Dept Physics York University Canada and Professor W. Happer Dept Physics Princeton University USA.

PART 4

IV.   CO2. THE BREATH OF LIFE.

Photosynthesis

The miracle of photosynthesis may perhaps be equalled in Nature but is never surpassed. It enables the conversion of solar radiated energy into stored chemical energy. By virtue of this process the gas CO_2 serves as the source of carbon for plant growth. The assimilation of CO_2 during photosynthesis forms a critical exchange between an atmospheric gas and the physiology of the Earth's biosphere within the global carbon cycle.

CO_2 is unique and indispensable. By it alone plants, including all trees, derive the carbon which is converted into sugars and starch by a process of carbon fixation using energy from sunlight and electrons from water. All other resources for plants, including nutrients and water, are derived from the soil. Moreover CO_2 is evenly distributed throughout the Earth's atmosphere. Accordingly, it affords similar access from plants across the entire terrestrial ecosystem. This distinguishes it from water, light and nutrients all of which vary across ecosystems and have much smaller scales.

However it is from the surface of the oceans that up to 75% of atmospheric oxygen is produced. Most of such production is from oceanic phytoplankton comprising one-celled drifting plants, algae, and some bacteria that can photosynthesize. One particular species, *Prochlorococcus bacterium*, is the smallest photosynthetic organism on Earth yet it produces up to 20% of the oxygen in our entire biosphere. This minute creature yields more oxygen than all of the Earth's tropical rainforests[106].

All of the oxygen we breathe is derived from CO_2 through photosynthesis. All plants and trees of every kind in terrestrial biosphere and all marine creatures or every kind owe their nutrition and growth to photosynthesis.

Carbon dioxide is the ultimate progenitor of oxygen and of all the plants that humanity and the animal kingdom require for life. To comprehend the impact of variations in the concentrations of atmospheric CO_2 it is necessary to examine those processes which are governed by or are directly concerned with atmospheric CO. These are:

- Photosynthesis itself.
- Cellular respiration.
- Transpiration.
- Photorespiration.

All of these processes are concerned with plant production or consumption of sugars and the conversion or exchange of carbon dioxide and oxygen. Diminishing concentrations of CO_2 have serious adverse consequences for plant growth, development, reproduction and survival. Higher concentrations of CO_2 produce substantial benefits in forestry, greening, crop yields and values.

The Greek components of the word *phōs* {φῶς} 'light' and *sunthesis* {σύνθεσις} 'creating or putting together' denote the essence of the process. Plants, algae and cyanobacteria convert the energy of sunlight into chemical energy which is synthesised from CO_2 and water. That energy is stored in carbohydrate molecules including sugar and starch. By cellular respiration it is made available for growth. The process involves release of O_2 {oxygen} as a waste product.

---

[106] National Oceanic and Atmospheric Agency USA ('NOAA')https://oceanservice.noaa.gov/facts/plankton.html.

RuBisCo is the accepted abbreviation for the enzyme Ribulose-1,5-bisphosphate carboxylase-oxygenase. It is the most common of all enzymes. A simple equation may help.

Figure 41

$$6CO_2 + 6H_2O \xrightarrow{\text{Light}} C_6H_{12}O_6 + 6O_2$$

Carbon dioxide   Water   Sugar   Oxygen

There are two stages in the process.

Light dependent process

Energy from sunlight is absorbed by proteins or reaction centres. These contain green pigmented chlorophyll and are held inside organelles, forms of microcompartments of a cell denoted chloroplasts. They are located in leaf cells of plants and the plasma membrane of bacteria. Water is necessary. It provides the electrons which are stripped by the sunlight energy from H_2O so producing oxygen. Hydrogen that is thus released is employed to create certain compounds which serve as temporary stores of energy. These compounds are *adenine dinucleotide phosphate* ('NADPH') and *adenosine triphosphate* ('ATP'). ATP is formed by the addition of a phosphate group to a molecule of adenosine diphosphate {'ADP'}.

Light independent process

The enzyme RuBisCo catalyses the reaction between Ribulose-1,5-bisphosphate (RuBP) - which is common to all plants – and CO_2 itself. It thereby captures atmospheric CO_2 and in a complex process {the Calvin cycle} takes up NADPH and ATP and releases 3-carbon sugars which then are combined to form sucrose and starch. This enables both regeneration of RuBP and also the formation of organic compounds required for growth, including cellulose for cell walls and ultimately amino acids and lipid used for storing energy and acting as structural components of cell membranes.

Extent of global photosynthesis

The scale of photosynthesis and of the energy and carbon that are involved is vast. The average rate of energy capture by photosynthesis described above is of the order of 130 terawatts. That is approximately 7.5 times the entire power consumption of humanity. Moreover each year over 100bn tons of carbon are converted into biomass of which cereals alone bind 3.8bn tons.

The following image depicts distribution of all terrestrial and oceanic photosynthesis with the deeper green and blue respectively indicating the intensive extents of photosynthetic conversion.

Figure 42

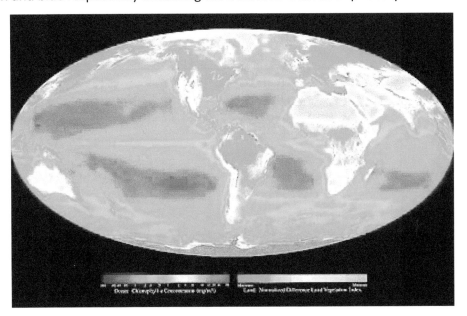

Cellular respiration

Respiration is the process of burning sugars to produce energy for living and growing. Plants respire: humans respire. The process is the obverse of photosynthesis. It involves the breaking down of sugar in the presence of oxygen to release energy in the form of ATP. This process releases carbon dioxide and water as waste products.

Photosynthesis converts CO_2 into carbohydrate using oxygen produced in the process. Cellular respiration uses molecules of oxygen to oxidise the carbohydrates and also amino acids and fatty acids to produce CO_2 and water whilst liberating ATP chemical energy to fuel the metabolism of the plant or other organism. This respiration occurs in the mitochondria[107] – a double-membrane- bound organelle of plant cells. It is a process that does not require light.

Transpiration

As noted above plants depend on water for photosynthesis. In capturing sunlight and CO_2, plants use light energy to split water molecules using their electrons to produce oxygen and hydrogen forming energy stores. Water is also essential for other processes namely:-

- the phenomenon known as turgor (hydrostatic pressure) whereby pressure exerted by fluid in a cell presses the membrane against the cell wall making the living plant rigid and upright.

- Transportation of chemicals and hormones from cell to cell particularly Auxins comprising plant hormones having a key role growth and behavioural processes in plant life cycles.

- Absorption of nutrients through roots by leaching of the dissolved nutrient elements enables transfer through root hairs through xylem 108, the plant vascular tissue, to stems and leaves.

- Dilution of waste especially within the vacuole which also assists with storage of water and with turgor.

Transpiration is the process of water migration through a plant and its evaporation from its air tangent parts – in particular its leaves. Water is absorbed at the roots by osmosis. Dissolved mineral nutrients travel with it through the xylem. Most of the water from roots is lost by transpiration leaving only a small proportion available to be used for growth and metabolism. There is a further loss through seeping from the tips or edges of leaves, mostly at night.

Leaf surfaces are pitted with stomata (pores) mainly on the undersides of the leaf. The stomata have guard cells and accessory cells known as the stomatal complex. These open and close the apertures. In the process of transpiration the stomata open to permit the essential ingress of CO_2 as well as the release of oxygen. It is by reason of the opening of the stomata apertures that the plant loses water escaping through the stomata in the process of transpiration.

This is of particular concern in the process of photorespiration occurring in C3 plants. Set out below is an image of stomata showing a guard cell open and another closed.

---

[107] Membrane covered organelles. Mitochondria are unique organelles that contain their own DNA. They produce the cell's energy through respiration.

[108] a tissue consisting of dead cells which transports water and minerals from the roots up the plant stem and into the leaves.

Figure 43

Transpiration also cools plants, changes osmotic pressure of cells and allows flow of nutrients and water from roots to shoots.

Plants regulate the rate of transpiration – the rate of CO_2 ingress and diffusion and the rate of water loss - by controlling the size of the stomatal apertures. The critical factor is the extent to which the stomata have to open to admit adequate CO_2 since the wider the aperture the more the loss of water through transpiration. When CO_2 density falls the stomata enlarge significantly to compensate thus curtailing growth through such water loss.

Increases in CO_2 atmospheric density diminish the number and aperture openings of stomata thus preserving water for the plant, minimizing inhibiting photorespiration and promoting growth.

Photorespiration

Photorespiration refers to a process in plant metabolism by which the enzyme RuBisCO takes effect to incorporate O_2 (oxygen) instead of CO_2 (carbon dioxide) so impeding growth of the plant. When it incorporates CO_2 it is said to act as a carboxylase. When it incorporates oxygen it acts as an oxygenase. At relatively high densities of CO_2 RuBisCo acts mainly as a carboxylase.

The addition of carbon dioxide to RuBP is a key step in the Calvin cycle of production of carbohydrates for the plant and the resulting oxygen emissions as explained above. RuBisCO procures the fixing of CO_2 to form sugar as energy for the plant and releasing an oxygen molecule. However RuBisCO may just as effectively fix oxygen instead of CO_2. However the addition of oxygen in place of CO_2 removes a critical part of the cycle.

Photorespiration in plants is thought to have risen over time and to have been the result of increasing levels of O_2 in the atmosphere - the by-product of photosynthetic organisms themselves. The reaction that is intended is the addition of carbon dioxide to RuBP which is a crucial step in the Calvin cycle. However for C3 plants at least 25% of RuBisCO reactions add oxygen to RuBP (oxygenation) creating products that cannot be used in the Calvin cycle.

Such oxygenation is wasteful in that considerable energy is used to turn the products of photorespiration back into a form that can react with CO_2. In particular an essential three-carbon compound is produced at a reduced rate and at higher metabolic cost in oxygenase activity compared with RuBP carboxylase activity. At least 25% of carbon fixed by photorespiration is re- released as CO_2 and nitrogen in the form of ammonia. Ammonia must then be detoxified at a substantial cost to the cell. Photorespiration also incurs a direct cost in ATP and NADPH.

Addition of molecular oxygen to RuBP produces phosphoglycolate which inhibits certain enzymes involved in photosynthetic carbon fixation. It is also difficult to recycle. In higher plants - a large group of plants that have veins to distribute resources through the plant - it is counteracted by a series of reactions in the peroxisome, mitochondria and again in the peroxisome. However in the metabolic pathway of this process - the conversion of glycolate to glyoxlate - hydrogen peroxide is produced in the peroxisome[109]. Hydrogen peroxide is a dangerous oxidant which has immediately to be split into water and oxygen by the enzyme catalase resulting ultimately in the release of CO_2 and ammonia {NH_3}.

This adverse combination of conditions is made worse in hot and dry conditions since plants close stomata to prevent water loss. This further diminishes CO_2 ingress. It also increases oxygen from light reactions of photosynthesis so intensifying photorespiration. This decreases carbon fixation for plant growth and development. The process reduces the efficiency of photosynthesis, diminishing photosynthetic output by at least 25% in the 90% of plants which together comprise the category of C3 plants.

However the increase in atmospheric CO_2 concentrations expected over the next 100 years will greatly reduce the rate of photorespiration in most plants by restricting water loss and thus will substantially enhance food production.

As is explained in greater detail in Section XIII the greater the CO_2 density the more effective is photosynthetic production of food. The planet is in a period of CO_2 famine. Levels of concentration have been 6 to 8 times higher during 99% of the geological past since the appearance of multicellular life forms 550m years ago {Figure 3}.

C4 plants

Over 90% of all plants use the carbon fixation process described above. They are known as C3 plants for the reason that they use the primary carboxylation reaction effected by RuBisCO to produce 3-phosphoglycerate {3 carbon atoms} in the Calvin cycle prior to ultimate reduction to carbohydrates and amino acids. The process of carbon fixation allows creation of sugars used for storage of energy.

C4 plants evolved due to the disadvantages to the process of photosynthesis due to the oxygenation of the Earth's atmosphere. They represent just 3% of all plants.

Recent studies indicate that photosynthesis first appeared as process in the biosphere 3.4bn years ago. In its earliest form the process was anoxygenic in that it converted light energy to ATP without using water as an electron donor so not requiring oxygen. Donors of electrons included chemical sources including hydrogen sulphide.

The origin of oxygenic photosynthesis was the most important metabolic innovation in Earth's history. It allowed life to generate energy and reducing power directly from sunlight and water, freeing it from the limited resources of geochemically derived reductants. Approximately 2.4bn years ago - and probably before - oxygenation of the atmosphere by cyanobacteria by oxygenic photosynthesis resulted in evolution of photosynthesis using water as an electron donor. This introduced oxygen into photosynthesis and opened the door for photorespiration.

To overcome the adverse impacts of photorespiration certain plants evolved the means of intensifying CO_2 concentrations in their leaves to compensate for the decline in carbon fixation. This is achieved by using the enzyme PEP[110] to create the 4 carbon compound acid oxaloacetate resulting in both the release of CO_2 and also its fixing by RuBisCO to the 3-phosphoglycerate {3 carbon atoms} of the Calvin cycle. Effectively this process divorces RuBisCO from the primary oxygen generating sunlight reactions and increases CO_2 fixation.

---

[109] A membrane-bound organelle, a type of microbody, found in the cytoplasm of virtually all cells having a defined nucleus. In plants fatty acids are broken down to carbon dioxide and water in peroxisomes.
[110] Phosphoenolpyruvate carbocylase.

Accordingly C4 plants suffer less from photorespiration and are able to produce more sugar than C3 plants provided that the sunlight is sufficiently intense and temperature sufficiently high. These C4 plants include sugarcane, maize, gluten free flour (sorghum) and millet.

Whilst the evolutionary solution to the disadvantages of photorespiration is very effective within the required conditions it is very limited in the extent of species within the biosphere to which it applies.

SUMMARY

By photosynthesis all plants and trees derive from CO_2 their sugar and starch stores of energy. All the oxygen we breathe comes from photosynthesis of CO_2 water and sunlight. All organic life in the biosphere including all humans, animals and all marine creatures depend on CO_2 for their existence.

XII.   CO₂ FAMINE & FOOD

It has to be understood that the levels of CO_2 in the atmosphere are today 3 times lower than the optimum required for crop growth, expansion of forestry and vegetation. For 395m years of the 400m years since plants and trees appeared on our planet CO_2 density in the atmosphere has been between 5 and 8 times the levels of the present day.

The effect of the appalling folly of Net Zero, if applied to all the peoples of the planet, would be the elimination of humanity and all organic life. Below 150 parts per million photosynthesis cannot occur. Vast extinctions would result.

CO₂ deprivation and extinctions

The decline of CO_2 concentrations in the atmosphere has been accompanied by truly catastrophic extinctions with the Permian – Triassic extinction almost eliminating all marine and terrestrial life. The following diagrams show extinction events and CO_2 levels of the past 550m years.

Figure 44

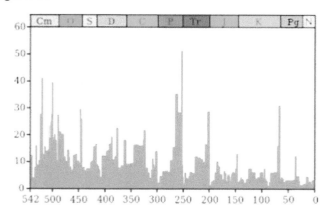

Figure 45

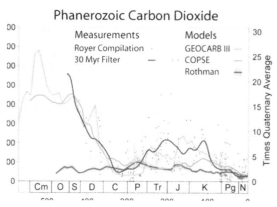

The mid to late Devonian period from 375–360m years ago saw a massive extinction with the collapse of CO_2 concentrations in the atmosphere by at least 50%. An extended series of extinctions removed more than 70% of all species[111].

CO_2 content of the atmosphere sustained a catastrophic fall to levels of between 300ppm to 400ppm in the period from 320m to 240m years ago in the Permian and early Triassic periods. This was accompanied (250 mya) by an extinction event exceeding all other such eliminations of life on Earth. 90% to 96% of species[112] vanished including the long enduring anthropod, the trilobite.

Figure 46

---

[111] Briggs, Derek; Crowther, Peter R. (2008). *Palaeobiology*. Vol. II. John Wiley & Sons. p. 223. ISBN 978-0-470-99928-8.

[112] Elewa AMT 2008 *Mass Extinction* Springer-Verlag cited in Plimer Op cit p175.

There was a relatively rapid and steep decline in CO_2 levels from 210mya to 190mya leading to the Triassic–Jurassic extinction event of 201mya. This rendered 70% to 75% of all species extinct and resulted in less competition for survival for the dinosaurs and so their consequent proliferation.

Effects of CO₂ famine

In the most recent lowest glacial maximum (the coldest period of an ice age) of 20,000 years ago CO_2 levels fell to between 180ppm and 190ppm[113]. There is abundant evidence that this severely constrained the physiological functioning of C3 plants.[114]

Studies have shown[115] that photosynthetic productivity of C3 plants is substantially reduced at these low CO_2 levels, particularly at higher temperatures and during stress. They have shown that plants have a limited capacity to modulate RubisCO and other photosynthetic proteins following falls of CO_2 concentrations.

It has been found[116] that at CO_2 levels of 200ppm – just 80ppm lower than the pre-industrial level – plants exhibit severe reductions in photosynthesis, growth, reproduction and survival and probable reduced tolerance to drought, heat and herbivory[117]. Within a single generation at such low levels collapse in biomass and photosynthesis ranges from 40% to 70%.[118] Even a reduction in CO_2 levels from 350ppm to just 270ppm - the pre-industrial level - results in a 24% reduction of biomass of C3 plants.[119]

The level of CO_2 content of the atmosphere is today only marginally higher than in the great Permian/Triassic extinction.

For humanity to be sure of surplus of food for its rising population it cannot entertain any assault on CO_2 – the very means by which such blessing may be brought about.

SUMMARY

For 395m years out of the 400m years since plants and trees appeared CO_2 density in the atmosphere has been up to 8 times higher than today.

A fall to pre-industrial levels of CO_2 will result in devastating declines in plant biomass and productivity. With CO_2 at 200ppm – only 80ppm lower than the pre-industrial level – plant biomass and photosynthesis is diminished by 40% to 70% within a single generation.

---

[113] Tripati et al 2009 *Coupling of CO₂ and ice sheet stability over major climate transitions of the last 20 million years.* Science 326 1394 – 1397.

[114] Polley et al *Increase of C3 plant water efficiency and biomass over glacial to present CO₂ concentrations* 1993 Nature 361 PP61 – 64. Ward JK et al *Carbon starvation in glacial trees recovered from the La Brea tar pits* 2005 Proceedings of the National Academy of Sciences USA 102 pp 690 – 694. Sage RF et al *Effects of low atmospheric CO₂ on plants* Trends in Plant Science 6 pp 18-24.

[115] Gerhart LM and Ward JK *Plant responses to low CO₂ of the past* 2010 New Phytologist 188 p 675.

[116] Studies cited in Gerhart LM and Ward JK *Plant responses to low CO₂ of the past* 2010 New Phytologist 188 p 675.

[117] The feeding on living plant parts by animal.

[118] Gerhart LM and Ward JK *Plant responses to low CO₂ of the past* 2010 New Phytologist 188 p 691.

[119] Dippery JK et al *Effects of low and elevated CO₂ on C£ and C$ annuals* Oecologia 995 101 pp13 – 20.

XIII.   CO₂ ABUNDANCE

There is a clear causal link between reduced stomatal density and rise of CO_2 concentrations in the atmosphere. With more abundant CO_2 the need for wide apertures to allow its absorption is diminished.

Effect on stomata and water loss

Increases in atmospheric CO_2 operate to close the apertures and diminish the density of stomata.

Indeed there is a close correlation of this process. One study has shown that during the rise of CO_2 density in the lifetime of a single birch tree during the then contemporary rise in atmospheric CO_2 (280ppm – 360ppm) stomatal density declined by 0.6% for every I ppm increase in CO_2.[120] A decrease of 30% in stomatal density was found to have occurred with the same rise of CO_2 over the period of its increase[121]. This has the effect of greatly reducing water loss.

The fundamental reason for the improved photosynthetic productivity and greatly reduced water loss through transpiration by way of the stomata is the increased density of CO_2 in the atmosphere. Stomata adjust to higher concentrations of CO_2 by having fewer apertures. Moreover the higher CO_2 content of the atmosphere itself diminishes photorespiration so further enhancing productivity.

These phenomena create food surpluses and transform the outlook for human welfare.

Greening

The CO_2 fertilization effect has dramatically intensified and enlarged since 1950 with the surge in annual emissions from 8bn tons to 35bn tons and atmospheric content from 300 ppm to 417 ppm.

Figure 47   **Figure 48**

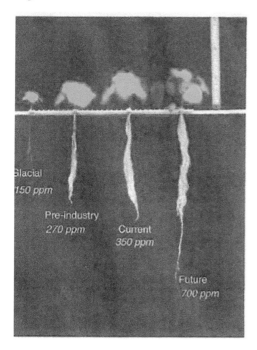
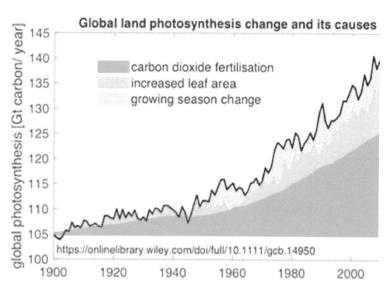

---

[120] *A natural experiment on plant acclimatation : lifetime stomatal frequency response of an individual tree to annual atmospheric CO_2 increase.* Proceedings of the National Academy of Science USA 93.pp11705 – 11708.

[121] *Evolutionary responses of land plants to atmospheric CO_2* Beerling DJ 2005 cited by Gerhart M. Ward JK Op cit.

The above diagrams[122] illustrate this remarkable change. The most recent significant extension of fertile land by reason of the CO_2 fertilisation effect is to be seen in the Sahel region immediately to the south of the Sahara desert.

The Sahel was an arid region. It extends from the Atlantic to the Red Sea which had suffered severe droughts in the 1960s and 1970s which were forced upon the population by decreased rainfall and the decline of precipitation of the West African Monsoon. Intensification of drought was predicted with famine seemingly bound to cause increasing mortality. The UN considered that for the people in the Sahel *"the outlook is bleak"* [123].

However over the past 12 years the boundary of the Sahara desert has steadily retreated. In the Sahel vegetation has become established on land formerly consisting of rocks and sand. In particular northern Burkina Faso has become greened to the extent that families exiled by drought to the coastal regions are returning to exploit the extraordinary improvement is grass and crop growth. C4 plants have seen an increase of no less than 70%. Production of millet in Burkina Faso since 1980 has risen by 55% and in Mali by 35%. Vegetation has extended in the last 15 years in southern Mauritania, North West Niger, central Chad, much of Sudan and even parts of Eritrea.

The following diagram shows the extent of greening of the Earth for the period from 1982 – 2015. It has been continuing unabated since then.

Figure 49

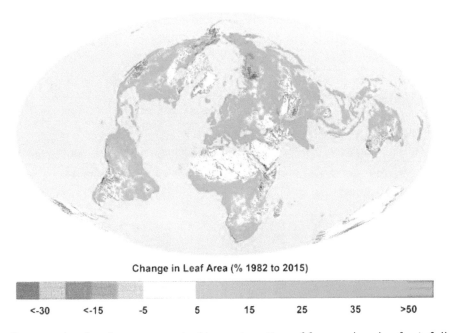

Change in Leaf Area (% 1982 to 2015)

| <-30 | <-15 | -5 | 5 | 15 | 25 | 35 | >50 |

The extension of vegetation has been prompted by restoration of former levels of rainfall. It is likely that higher temperature over the Sahara has encouraged movement of cooler moist air moving in from the Atlantic where surface temperature is appreciably lower. Rainfall, however, cannot account these observed trends. There are regions of the planet that have been shown as experiencing greening in the absence of any rainfall increase.[124] The critical factor is the impact of the higher density of atmospheric CO_2.

---

[122] Figure 47 Representative plants Abutilon theophrasti (velvetleaf or lantern mallow) a modern C4 annual. All plants grown under similar water, light and Nutrient conditions Dippery et at Op cit.

[123] IRIN, *Sahel: Backgrounder on the Sahel, West Africa's poorest region*, 2 June 2008, available at: https://www.refworld.org/docid/4847bb8f0.html [accessed 19 March 2022] *"UN Environment Programme (UNEP) says most climate models for the Sahel do predict drier conditions for the future"*.

[124] Fensholt R et al Greenness in semi-arid areas across the globe 1981 – 2007. An Earth observing satellited base analysis of trends and drivers Remote Sensing Environmental. 121. Pp144 – 158. SCIENTIFIC REPORTS 12 February 2015 Xuefei Lu et al.

During the period 1960 – 2015 CO_2 in the atmosphere increased by 28% from 315ppm to 405ppm. It is this that ensures that water remains in the root system and in the structure of plants without being lost through transpiration due to wide open stomata. It accounts for the permanent improvement in crop yields together with increased precipitation of water vapour due to the gradual and continuous transpiration from the expanding vegetation. It is the indirect water response of plants to elevated CO_2 that is the key. This has been shown[125] to improve soil water response by 89% in 'drylands.'[126]

The trend in extension of vegetation is repeated across all regions of the planet as is evident from Figure 49. In particular Southern Europe, China, India, North America and Eastern Russia have experienced intense and widespread greening over vast regions.

Growth in crop yields

The boon for humanity of this surge in plant growth and crop yields with increases in CO_2 was predicted by Professor Sylvan Wittwer in 1995[127]. Describing these as the one global natural resource that is progressively increasing food production and total biological output he stated that

"The rising level of atmospheric CO_2 is a means of inadvertently increasing the productivity of farming systems and other photosynthetically active ecosystems. The effects know no boundaries and both developing and developed countries are and will be sharing equally [for] the rising level of atmospheric CO_2 is a universally free premium, gaining in magnitude with time on which we all can reckon for the foreseeable future"

Figure 50

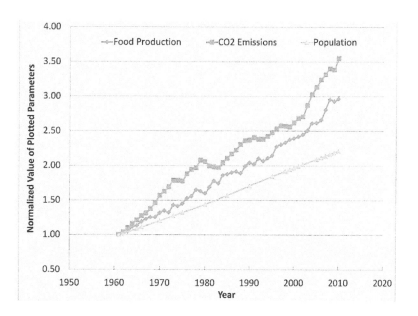

Figure 50[128] defines the correlation of global population increase, CO_2 emissions and food production over the period 1961 – 2010. It has been normalized to a value of unity at 1961. Accordingly, a data value of 2 represents a value that is twice the reported amount in 1961. Food production data represent the total production of the 45 crops that supplied 95% of total world food production.

[125] Lu, X. *et al*. Elevated CO_2 as a driver of global dryland greening. *Sci. Rep.* **6**, 20716; doi: 10.1038/srep20716 (2016).
[126] The United Nations Environment Programme (UNEP) defines drylands according to an aridity index (AI), which is the ratio between average annual precipitation and potential evapotranspiration; drylands are lands with an AI of less than 0.65.
[127] Sylvan Harold Wittwer (January 17, 1917 – January 20, 2012) Director Emeritus of the Michigan State University Agricultural Experiment Station and Professor of Horticulture., Author of *Feeding a Billion: Advancing Frontiers of Chinese Agriculture, (1987)* and *Food, Climate, and Carbon Dioxide: The Global Environment and World Food Production (1995).*
[128] *The Positive Externalities of Carbon Dioxide* Idso CD Center for the Study of Carbon Dioxide and Global Change 2013 p24.

Each of the three data sets experienced rapid and interlinked growth over 5 decades which is continuing.

A persistent and widespread increase of growing season and integrated leaf area index (greening) over 25% to 50% of the global vegetated area occurred between 1982 and 2009. CO_2 fertilization effects accounted for 70% of this satellite observed greening trend[129]. There is no doubt that the process has since accelerated with rising atmospheric CO_2 over the succeeding 13 years.

Optimum CO_2 atmospheric density

At current levels of 417 ppm we are in an extended period of CO_2 famine – see Section XII.

For 99% of time since the emergence of vegetation of all kinds over 400m years ago concentrations of CO_2 in the atmosphere have exceeded current levels by up to 8 orders of magnitude.

Land plants emerged in the middle Cambrian–early Ordovician periods 530mya – 480mya being periods in which density of atmospheric CO_2 varied from 5,500ppm – 4,500ppm. Modern form plants (vascular plants or tracheophytes) appeared in a Late Ordovician–Silurian interval about 420mya with CO_2 atmospheric concentrations of 4,300ppm – 4,000ppm. The earliest trees appeared 370mya ago in the mid Devonian period when CO_2 density was 3,700 – 4000 ppm.

The effect of such high densities was the extreme proliferation of all manner of vegetation over the entire land mass of the Earth drawing down vast volumes of CO_2. The following diagrams illustrate the appearance and expansion of vegetation across geological time. The maximum CO_2 levels after the initial Cambrian of 550mya are at the commencement of the Earth's greening and account for its dramatic extension over the planet.

Figure 51   **Figure 52**

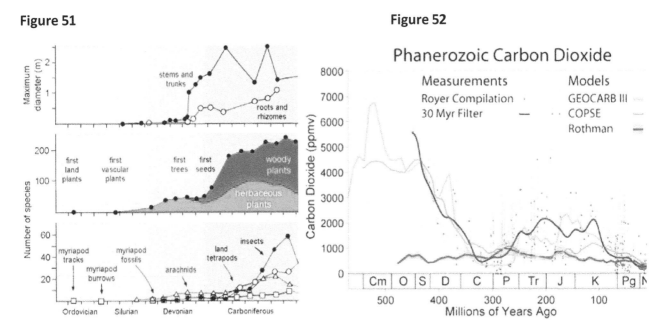

It with this in mind that consideration needs to be given to optimum densities of atmospheric CO_2 for crop growth, reproduction and development. These will produce surplus food for all.

As long ago as 1982 the International Conference on Rising Atmospheric Carbon Dioxide and Plant Productivity concluded that doubling of CO_2 density from 340ppm was likely to bring about a 50%

---

[129] Zaichun Zhu, Shilong Pia et al Greening of the Earth and its drivers. 2016 Nature Climate Change.

increase in plant photosynthesis. It predicted this would double water use efficiency in both C3 and C4 plants together with substantial increase in nitrogen fixation in most biological systems.[130]

Disregarding the concomitant beneficial influence of increased temperature there is much guidance as to the optimum levels of CO_2 for plant productivity from Government departments of agriculturally intensive regions.

Guidance from Oklahoma State University advised that an increase in ambient to 800-1000 ppm can increase yield of C_3 plants by up to 100 percent and C_4 plants by 25 percent.[131] Published guidance in Canada advises that increasing the CO_2 level to 1,000 ppm will increase photosynthesis by about 50% over ambient CO_2 levels. It advises that for most crops the saturation point will be reached at about 1,000–1,300 ppm[132]. This guidance is reflected in the following graph of the effect of increased CO_2 density in the production of cannabis[133].

Figure 53

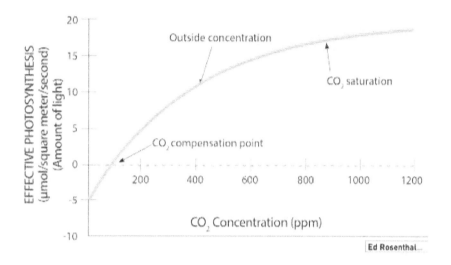

The 'compensation point' is that at which the rate of photosynthesis CO_2 influx equals the rate of release of CO_2 by leaf cellular respiration or by photorespiration. It will be seen that the increase of effective photosynthesis is still ascending even at 1,200ppm.

The following graphs Figures 54 – 56 chart the impact of rising CO_2 on crop yields and land use. Figure 54 tracks rise of CO_2 density and emissions. Figure 55 charts the increases in crop productivity in European countries since 1960 when CO_2 atmospheric levels began to rise steeply. There have been well over 100% increases of yields in the UK, Germany, Netherlands, Belgium, Denmark and France.

Figure 56 shows the proportion of land use diminishing in relation to crop yields over the same period. Although improvements in technology and fertilisers account for some of this beneficial improvement there can be no doubt that the increase of CO_2 is in perfect correlation and that it is the most important contributor.

---

[130] *Positive Externalities of Carbon Dioxide* Idso C.D. Center for the Study of Carbon Dioxide and Global Change 21.10.2013 p6.
[131] Greenhouse Carbon Dioxide Supplementation Published Mar. 2017|Id: HLA-6723 Megha Poudel, Bruce Dunn.
[132] Ontario Ministry of Agriculture Food and Rural Affairs.. Factsheet Carbon Dioxide in Greenhouses, Order No. 94-055. T.J Blom; W.A. Straver; F.J. Ingratta; Shalin Khosla – OMAFRA; Wayne Brown – OMAFRA
[132] *Why Plants Suffer If They Don't Get At Least A Minimum Amount Of CO2.* Ed Rosenthal 2018 www.edrosethal.com.

Figure 54

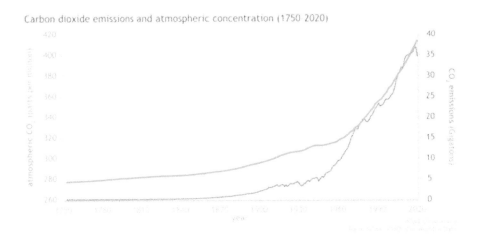

Carbon dioxide emissions and atmospheric concentration (1750 2020)

Figure 54 shows increases in CO_2 concentrations with the spike from 1960. Figures 55 and 56 show growth in yields and land productivity since 1960 when CO_2 concentrations intensified.

Figure 55

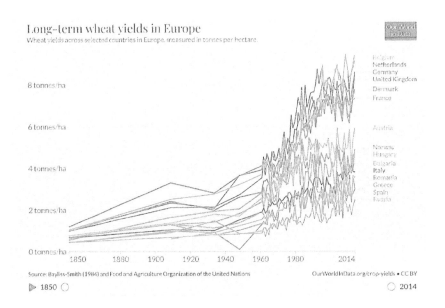

Figure 56

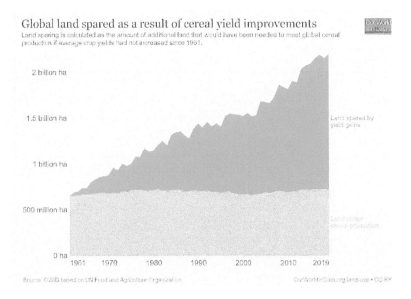

The correspondence between the gradients of CO_2 increase, rises in crop yields and land productivity is striking.

70

It is therefore no more than a prudent estimate that increases of atmospheric CO_2 by 3 orders of magnitude will more than double plant productivity with no noticeable impact on temperature.

Benefits of rising temperature

Most biological processes intensify with increasing temperature. So it is with the rate of photosynthesis. However the optimum temperature for maximum photosynthesis depends on the extent of the availability of CO_2. The more the concentration of atmospheric CO_2 the higher is the optimum temperature for crops.

Enhancement of plant growth is impelled by higher temperature in conjunction with increasing density of atmospheric CO_2. This highly beneficial phenomenon has been repeatedly demonstrated. As long ago as 1984[134] experimental observations of bigtooth aspen leaves under varying atmospheric CO_2 concentrations of 325ppm – 1,935ppm produced findings as follows.

Figure 57

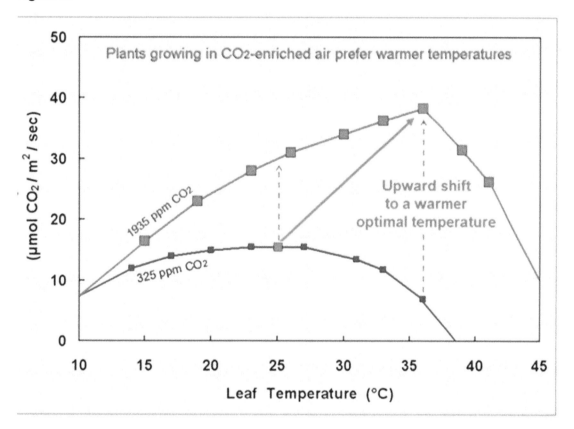

As shown in Figure 57 at 10°C elevated CO_2 has very little effect on net photosynthesis. But at 25°C, at which the photosynthetic rate at 325ppm of CO_2 is at its maximum, it will be seen that additional CO_2 increased the rate of photosynthesis by just under 100%. At 36°C, at which the photosynthetic rate at 1,935ppm of CO_2 is at its maximum, CO_2 has the effect of enhancing the rate of photosynthesis by 450%.

---

[134] Short-Term Effects of CO_2 on Gas Exchange of Leaves of Bigtooth Aspen (*Populus grandidentata*) in the Field 1 Thomas W. Jurik, James A. Weber, David M. Gates *Plant Physiology*, Volume 75, Issue 4, August 1984, Pages 1022–1026, https://doi.org/10.1104/pp.75.4.1022.

Many studies have shown that a 300ppm increase in atmospheric CO_2 raised the optimum temperature for plant growth by about 6^0C[135]. Such a response more than compensates for any temperature induced stress from even the most exaggerated temperature increase predictions of the IPCC none of which have been fulfilled.

A compelling observational experiment – not a speculative modelling – was conducted in 2010[136]. Investigation was made into photosynthetic sensitivity to temperature[137]. It extended to the potential for adapting to a new climate conditions of five species of deciduous trees. This was done outside in open- top chambers maintained at three different temperature regimes -- ambient and ambient plus 2°C and 4°C above ambient -- for a period of three years.

The warming treatments resulted in a shift in response of CO_2 assimilation, such that leaves in warmer treatments had higher temperature optima as depicted in the figure below. It was found that this adjustment was effected in as little as 2 – 6 days and applied to all species.

Figure 58

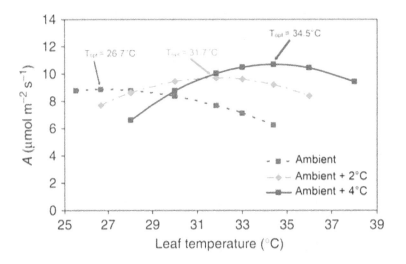

Net CO_2 assimilation rate vs. leaf temperature in Quercus rubra seedlings during June of 2003 in the ambient (A) and elevated (A+2°C and A+4°C) temperature treatments.

It is thus demonstrated that, over a representative range of species[138], trees can adjust their physiology not just to survive warming of 2°C – 4°C – even if instantaneous – but actually to benefit from it.

Accordingly with the aerial fertilization effect of rising atmospheric CO_2 concentrations, taken with its transpiration-reducing effect that vastly increases tree water use efficiency, the Earth's forests possess the ideal combination of conditions to support a very extensive greening of the planet. It is most probable that this will continue to the great welfare and prosperity of humanity.

[135] *The State of the Earth's Terrestrial Biosphere: How is it Responding to Rising Atmospheric CO_2 and Warmer Temperatures* 2022 Center for the Study of Carbon Dioxide and Global Change co2science.org/education /reports /greening /the future php. [136] Gunderson, L. 2010. *Ecological and human community resilience in response to natural disasters. Ecology and Society* 15(2): 18. [online] URL: http://www.ecologyandsociety.org/vol15/iss2/art18/.
[137] Gunderson, C.A., O'Hara, K.H., Campion, C.M., Walker, A.V. and Edwards, N.T. 2010. *Thermal plasticity of photosynthesis: the role of acclimation in forest responses to a warming climate.* Global Change Biology 2010 – 16: pp2272-2286.
[138] *Liquidambar styraciflua* [sweetgum], *Quercus rubra* [northern red oak], *Quercus falcata* [southern red oak], *Betula alleghaniensis* [yellow birch] and *Populus grandidentata* [bigtooth aspen].

Crop values: the CO₂ effect

As has been explained above it has been found that doubling the concentration of atmospheric CO_2 is likely to bring about a 50% increase in plant growth even on the most prudent estimate. Many studies have also shown that a 300ppm increase in atmospheric CO_2 raises the optimum temperature for plant growth by about 6°C[139]. At 25°C at which the photosynthetic rate at 325ppm of CO_2 is at its maximum – it has been seen that additional CO_2 increased the rate of photosynthesis by just under 100%. At higher CO_2 concentrations and increased temperature photosynthetic yields are increased by many orders of magnitude.

These increases give rise to formidable rises in crop yields.

Many studies testify to this great benefit to humanity. It has prompted research into the monetary benefit that increase of CO_2 density has conferred since the pre-industrial level of 280ppm. It has enabled estimates to be made of net wealth that resulting increases in crop yields will produce based on known factors underlying the assumptions made in support.

The UN Food and Agriculture Organisation ('UNFOA') publishes annual global crop yield and crop production data. The monetary value as to such production are published in the UNFOA statistical database ('UNFAOSTAT') covering 245 countries from 1961 to the most recent available date.

Using the UNFAOSTAT data a comprehensive study of the benefits in money terms of rise in atmospheric CO_2 was published in 2013[140]. It is a detailed and fully quantified analysis. The summary given below necessarily condenses the key elements of the research and reference must be made to the full report for its full data, meaning and effect.

The study provides a quantitative estimate of the direct monetary benefits of atmospheric CO_2 enrichment on historic global crop production over the 50 year period to 2011 and future production. Results indicate that the annual total monetary value of the effect of increase in CO_2 atmospheric content since the pre-industrial era on world crop production grew from $18.5 billion in 1961 to over $140 billion by 2011, reaching the staggering sum of $3.2 trillion over the 50-year period from 1961-2011. Projecting the monetary value of this positive effect forward in time it is estimated to bestow an additional $9.8 trillion on crop production between 2011 and 2050.

The study took account of 45 crops in the top 95% of world food production. These are set out in Appendix A. Plant specific growth enhancement responses to increasing CO_2 were acquired from the Plant Growth Database of CO2 Science[141] and calculation was made of crop growth percentage increases in response to a 300ppm increase in atmospheric CO_2 as set out in Appendix B.

To establish monetary benefit a calculation was made of what proportion of each annual yield over the 50 year period of each crop was due to CO_2 increase over the base of 280ppm. Applying the UNFAOSTAT gross production value in constant 2004-2006 US dollars of each crop per metric ton it was possible to estimate the annual monetary benefit of atmospheric CO_2 enrichment above 280ppm over the 50 year period.

Appendix C sets out the monetary benefits so calculated.

The benefits for each of the 45 crops examined amounted to at least $1bn. For 9 of those crops the benefit was over $100bn with rice at $579bn, wheat at $274bn and grapes at $270bn. These

---

[139] *The State of the Earth's Terrestrial Biosphere: How is it Responding to Rising Atmospheric CO₂ and Warmer Temperatures* 2022 Science Center for the Study of Carbon Dioxide and Global Change www.co2science.org/education/reports/greening /thefuture.php.

[140] *The Positive Externalities of Carbon Dioxide* October 2013 Center for the Study of Carbon Dioxide and Global Change Op cit.

[141] http://www.co2science.org/about/web_features.php.

calculations are made on yield values that are net of other factors that might tend to influence crop yield over the 50 year period. These are referred to in the 2013 report as the *'techno-intel effect'* since it derives primarily from ongoing advances in agricultural technology and scientific research which together enlarged the knowledge or intelligence base.

The momentous impact on human wealth creation of an increase to just 580ppm atmospheric CO_2 over a 50 year period justifies confidence that a 3 fold increase over today's levels will be to create a vast store of food and wealth for all mankind.

Conclusion

Given the myriad blessings of carbon and of carbon dioxide to humanity's very existence, welfare and prosperity is it not astonishing that the US Environmental Protection Agency should have declared CO_2 to be harmful to both people and to the environment.

It is hard to conceive of a statement which owes so little to the truth.

SUMMARY

CO_2 induced reduction of water loss and decline in photorespiration together with intensified CO_2 fertilisation accounted for at least 70% of satellite observed global greening of between 25% to 50% occurring 1982 – 2009. Increase in CO_2 concentrations to 1000 - 1200 ppm increase yields by up to 100 percent.

Adding more CO_2 to the atmosphere raises the optimum temperature for net photosynthesis due to less water loss and minimal photorespiration. At over 4 times present density and up to 36^{0}C the rate of photosynthesis rises by a multiple of 4.5.

UN data on crop production from 1961 – 2011 provide a calculated value of increased crop yields of $3.2 trillion as a consequence of enrichment by increasing CO_2. Estimates to 2050 are more than double.

Carbon dioxide is the most potent natural factor in the relief of world hunger and poverty. It is indispensable to our existence.

APPENDIX

The following is reproduced from the "The Positive Externalities of Carbon Dioxide: Estimating the Monetary Benefits of Rising Atmospheric CO_2 Concentrations on Global Food Production"

Center for the Study of Carbon Dioxide and Global Change a non-profit organization based in Tempe USA.

"The first step in determining the monetary benefit of historical atmospheric CO_2 enrichment on historic crop production begins by calculating what portion of each crop's annual yield over the period 1961-2011 was due to each year's increase in atmospheric CO_2 concentration above the baseline value of 280 ppm that existed at the beginning of the Industrial Revolution.

Illustrating this process for wheat, in 1961 the global yield of wheat from the FAOSTAT database was 10,889 hectograms per hectare (Hg/Ha), the atmospheric CO_2 concentration was 317.4 ppm, represent ing an increase of 37.4 ppm above the 280-ppm baseline, while the CO_2 growth response factor for wheat as listed in Table 2 is 34.9% for a 300-ppm increase in CO_2. To determine the impact of the 37.4 ppm rise in atmospheric CO_2 on 1961 wheat yields, the wheat- specific CO_2 growth response factor of 34.9% per 300 ppm CO_2 increase (mathematically written as 34.9%/300 ppm) is multiplied by the 37.4 ppm increase in CO_2 that has occurred since the Industrial Revolution. The resultant value of 4.35% indicates the degree by which the 1961 yield was enhanced above the baseline yield value corresponding to an atmospheric CO_2 concentration of 280 ppm. The 1961 yield is then divided by this relative increase (1.0435) to determine the baseline yield in Hg/Ha (10,889/1.0435 = 10,435). The resultant baseline yield amount of 10,435 Hg/Ha is subtracted from the 1961 yield total of 10,889 Hg/Ha, revealing that 454 Hg/Ha of the 1961 yield was due to the 37.4 ppm rise in CO_2 *since the start of the Industrial Revolution*. Sim- ilar calculations are then made for each of the remaining years in the 50-year period, as well as for each of the 44 remaining crops accounting for 95% of global food production.

The next step is to determine what *percentage* of the total annual yield of each crop in each year was due to CO_2. This was accomplished by simply taking the results calculated in the previous step and dividing them by the corresponding total annual yields. For example, using the calculations for wheat from above, the 454 Hg/Ha yield due to CO_2 in 1961 was divided by the total 10,889 Hg/Ha wheat yield for that year, revealing that 4.17% of the total wheat yield in 1961 was due to the historical rise in atmospheric CO_2. Again, such percentage calculations were completed for all crops for each year in the 50-year period 1961-2011.

Knowing the annual percentage influences of CO_2 on all crop *yields* (production per Ha), the next step is to determine how that influence is manifested in total *crop production value*. This was accomplished by multiplying the CO_2-induced yield percentage increases by the corresponding annual *production* of each crop, and by then multiplying these data by the gross

production *value* (in constant 2004-2006 U.S. dollars) of each crop per metric ton, which data were obtained from the FAOSTAT database, the end result of which calculations becomes an estimate of the *annual monetary benefit* of atmospheric CO_2 enrichment (above the baseline of 280 ppm) on crop production since 1961. And these monetary values are presented for each of the 45 crops under examination in Table 3."

Global crop yields and production data from the UN Food and Agriculture Organization.

Table 1 The forty-five crops forming 95% of the total world food production over the period 1961-2011.

Crop	% of Total Production	Crop	% of Total Production
Sugar cane	20.492	Rye	0.556
Wheat	10.072	Plantains	0.528
Maize	9.971	Yams	0.523
Rice, paddy	9.715	Groundnuts, with shell	0.518
Potatoes	6.154	Rapeseed	0.494
Sugar beet	5.335	Cucumbers and gherkins	0.492
Cassava	3.040	Mangoes, mangosteens, guavas	0.406
Barley	2.989	Sunflower seed	0.398
Vegetables fresh nes	2.901	Eggplants (aubergines)	0.340
Sweet potatoes	2.638	Beans, dry	0.331
Soybeans	2.349	Fruit Fresh Nes	0.321
Tomatoes	1.571	Carrots and turnips	0.320
Grapes	1.260	Other melons (inc.cantaloupes)	0.302
Sorghum	1.255	Chillies and peppers, green	0.274
Bananas	1.052	Tangerines, mandarins, clem.	0.264
Watermelons	0.950	Lettuce and chicory	0.262
Oranges	0.935	Pumpkins, squash and gourds	0.248
Cabbages and other brassicas	0.903	Pears	0.243
Apples	0.886	Olives	0.241
Coconuts	0.843	Pineapples	0.230
Oats	0.810	Fruit, tropical fresh nes	0.230
Onions, dry	0.731	Peas, dry	0.228
Millet	0.593		
Sum of All Crops = 95.2%			

Table 2 Mean crop growth response for each crop listed in Table 1 to a 300-ppm rise in atmospheric CO_2

Crop	% Biomass Change	Crop	% Biomass Change
Sugar cane	34.0%	Rye	38.0%
Wheat	34.9%	Plantains	44.8%
Maize	24.1%	Yams	47.0%
Rice, paddy	36.1%	Groundnuts, with shell	47.0%
Potatoes	31.3%	Rapeseed	46.9%
Sugar beet	65.7%	Cucumbers and gherkins	44.8%
Cassava	13.8%	Mangoes, mangosteens, guavas	36.0%
Barley	35.4%	Sunflower seed	36.5%
Vegetables fresh nes	41.1%	Eggplants (aubergines)	41.0%
Sweet potatoes	33.7%	Beans, dry	61.7%
Soybeans	45.5%	Fruit Fresh Nes	72.3%
Tomatoes	35.9%	Carrots and turnips	77.8%
Grapes	68.2%	Other melons (inc.cantaloupes)	4.7%
Sorghum	19.9%	Chillies and peppers, green	41.1%
Bananas	44.8%	Tangerines, mandarins, clem.	29.5%
Watermelons	41.5%	Lettuce and chicory	18.5%
Oranges	54.9%	Pumpkins, squash and gourds	41.5%
Cabbages and other brassicas	39.3%	Pears	44.8%
Apples	44.8%	Olives	35.2%
Coconuts	44.8%	Pineapples	5.0%
Oats	34.8%	Fruit, tropical fresh nes	72.3%
Onions, dry	20.0%	Peas, dry	29.2%
Millet	44.3%		

Table 3

The total monetary benefit of Earth's rising atmospheric CO_2 concentration on each of the forty- five crops listed in Table 1 for the 50-year period 1961-2011. Values are in constant 2004-2006 U.S. dollars.

Crop	Production Rank	Monetary Benefit of CO_2	Crop	Production Rank	Monetary Benefit of CO_2
Rice, paddy	4	$579,013,089,273	Carrots and turnips	35	$36,439,812,318
Wheat	2	$274,751,908,146	Cucumbers and gherkins	29	$33,698,222,461
Grapes	13	$270,993,488,618	Watermelons	16	$32,553,055,795
Maize	3	$182,372,524,324	Pears	41	$31,577,067,767
Soybeans	11	$148,757,417,756	Fruit Fresh Nes	34	$29,182,817,600
Potatoes	5	$147,862,516,739	Fruit, tropical fresh nes	44	$28,837,991,342
Vegetables fresh nes	9	$143,295,147,644	Millet	23	$24,748,422,190
Tomatoes	12	$140,893,704,588	Eggplants (aubergines)	32	$22,794,746,004
Sugar cane	1	$107,420,713,630	Cassava	7	$21,850,017,436
Apples	19	$98,329,393,797	Onions, dry	22	$20,793,394,925
Sugar beet	6	$69,247,223,819	Sorghum	14	$20,579,850,257
Barley	8	$63,046,887,462	Tangerines, mandarins, clem.	38	$18,822,174,419
Bananas	15	$58,264,644,460	Coconuts	20	$17,949,253,896
Yams	26	$56,163,446,226	Sunflower seed	31	$17,585,395,685
Groundnuts, with shell	27	$51,076,843,461	Plantains	25	$17,384,141,669
Olives	42	$50,604,186,875	Lettuce and chicory	39	$15,029,691,577
Oranges	17	$50,173,178,154	Pumpkins, squash and gourds	40	$13,140,422,653
Beans, dry	33	$47,240,266,167	Oats	21	$12,615,396,815
Mangoes, mangosteens, guavas	30	$40,731,776,757	Rye	24	$8,981,587,998
Sweet potatoes	10	$39,889,080,598	Peas, dry	45	$5,667,935,087
Chillies and peppers, green	37	$39,813,008,532	Other melons (inc.cantaloupes)	36	$2,477,799,109
Rapeseed	28	$38,121,172,234	Pineapples	43	$1,779,091,848
Cabbages and other brassicas	18	$37,501,047,431		Sum of all crops =	$3,170,050,955,544

The Bruges Group is an independent all-party think tank. Set up in 1989, its founding purpose was to resist the encroachments of the European Union on our democratic self-government. The Bruges Group spearheaded the intellectual battle to win a vote to leave the European Union and against the emergence of a centralised EU state. With personal freedom at its core, its formation was inspired by the speech of Margaret Thatcher in Bruges in September 1988 where the Prime Minister stated, "We have not successfully rolled back the frontiers of the State in Britain only to see them re-imposed at a European level."

We now face a more insidious and profound challenge to our liberties – the rising tide of intolerance. The Bruges Group challenges false and damaging orthodoxies that suppress debate and incite enmity. It will continue to direct Britain's role in the world, act as a voice for the Union, and promote our historic liberty, democracy, transparency, and rights. It spearheads the resistance to attacks on free speech and provides a voice for those who value our freedoms and way of life.

The Bruges Group holds regular high–profile public meetings, seminars, debates and conferences. These enable influential speakers to contribute to the European debate. Speakers are selected purely by the contribution they can make to enhance the debate.

For further information about the Bruges Group, to attend our meetings, or join and receive our publications, please see the membership form at the end of this paper. Alternatively, you can visit our website www.brugesgroup.com or contact us at info@brugesgroup.com.

Contact us

For more information about the Bruges Group please contact:
Robert Oulds, Director
The Bruges Group, 246 Linen Hall, 162-168 Regent Street, London W1B 5TB
Tel: +44 (0)20 7287 4414 **Email:** info@brugesgroup.com

www.brugesgroup.com

www.brugesgroup.com

DONATE TO THE BRUGES GROUP

Yes, I wish to donate to *The Bruges Group*

☐ £5   ☐ £10   ☐ £20   ☐ £50   ☐ £100   ☐ £250   ☐ £500   ☐ £1,000

Other please specify:...

DONATIONS BY CHEQUE / POSTAL ORDER

Title: .... First Name:..

Surname: ....

Address: ....

.... Postcode ....

Email:...

Telephone: ....

Signature: .... Date:......................................

PLEASE MAKE CHEQUES PAYABLE TO *THE BRUGES GROUP*
PLEASE RETURN THIS FORM TOGETHER WITH YOUR DONATION TO:
The Bruges Group, 246 Linen Hall, 162-168 Regent Street, London W1B 5TB

DONATIONS BY CREDIT / DEBIT CARDS

☐ MasterCard   ☐ VISA   ☐   ☐ JCB   MasterPass   ☐ Maestro

Card number [   ]

Valid from [   ]   Expiry date [   ]   Issue number [   ]   Security code [   ]

Card holder's name as it appears on the card (please print):..

....

Address of card holder: ....

.... Postcode ....

Email:...

Telephone: ....

Signature: .... Date:......................................

OR AT ANY BARCLAYS BANK

Account Name: The Bruges Group **Sort Code:** 20-46-73 **Account number:** 90211214

FOR DONATIONS OVER THE PHONE CALL OUR HOTLINE ON 020 7287 4414

Secure online donations can be made via our website at **www.brugesgroup.com/donate**
Donations can be made via credit / debit cards

DONATIONS BY STANDING ORDER

Yes, I wish to donate to *The Bruges Group*

Title: .... First Name:..

Surname: ....

Address: ....

....

.... Postcode..

Email:..

Telephone: ....

Please complete this form in BLOCK CAPITALS and return it to us at the address overleaf.

To: The Manager, ... Bank/Building Society

Branch Address:..

....

....Postcode: ....

Your Account Number ☐☐☐☐☐☐☐☐   Sort code ☐☐ ☐☐ ☐☐

Please pay Barclays Bank PLC (sort code 20-46-73) 6 Clarence Street, Kingston-upon-Thames, Surrey KT1 1NY

The sum of (please tick as appropriate) ☐ £10 ☐ £20 ☐ £50 ☐ £100 ☐ £250 ☐ £500 ☐ £1,000

☐ Other, please specify: ....

....Amount in words

To the credit of *The Bruges Group*, Account Number 90211214
forthwith and on the same day in each subsequent **year** or **month** *(please circle your preference)* until further notice.

Signature: .... Date:..

Please print name and title:..

9 781838 065867